£15

INTERNATIONAL POULTRY LIBRARY

BANTAMS
&
SMALL POULTRY

Illustration of Early Bantams drawn by Harrison Weir
**Historically   very significant; showing Old English Game
bantams before Modern Game became popular (c 1858)**

BANTAMS
&
SMALL POULTRY

JOSEPH BATTY

Beech Publishing House
Station Yard
ELSTED
Midhurst
West Sussex   GU29 0JT

ISBN 1-85736-174-1

Beech Publishing House
Station Yard
ELSTED
Midhurst
West Sussex   GU29 0JT

Printed and bound in Great Britain

FOREWORD

Bantams are diminutive fowl, originally from far off lands, which possess great charm and, often, utility properties, and are part of a growing pastime. Its main feature is the keeping of small livestock which is a relaxing hobby and, in the right hands, a profitable one.

Breeds of bantams are to be found in a wide and diverse range. Some came from China, others Japan, and many were developed from breeds of large fowl. Generally, they are 25 per cent of the size of the equivalent large fowl.

A number are 'ornamental' types, which possess some remarkable feature, such as feathered legs, beards, exotic plumage or some other feature. Others are layers which produce a good supply of eggs.

Many bantam fanciers show their birds and follow the poultry *standards* in the particular poultry club in their own country.

This guide to the breeds is written in a concise fashion, and each bird is shown, where practicable, in a photograph or drawing. The selected colour plates show the beauty and diversity of these fascinating birds.

My thanks are offered to authors, fanciers and clubs who supplied details, drawings or photograph; without them a work of this kind would not be possible. In the UK there are too many to name individually, but from the USA special mention should be made of Fred P Jeffrey, and Loyl Stromberg who have done so much work in the poultry fancy and despite being 'retired' are still involved.

J Batty

CONTENTS

A Note on the Origin of the Bantams
The Poultry Yard
Miss E Watts (c. 1858)

The Bankiva jungle fowl may be the origin of our Bantam breeds; the term Bantam would seem to establish the fact. Bantam is the name of a town and district in the north-west of Java...........
In 1595 the Dutch established themselves at Bantam, and in 1602 the English erected a factory in the same place, which was the first possession of the English in the East Indies. ......it is evident that the beautiful Bankiva jungle fowls, reclaimed by the natives, and sold to the British at Bantam, while their factory was established there, were imported into England under the very natural appellation of Bantam fowls. Their elegance and diminutive size rendered them favourites, and in due time the name, belonging exclusively to these birds, came to be conferred on all small or dwarf fowls.

These extracts from the very well researched book of Miss Watts seems quite conclusive as regards the origin of the name 'Bantam'. Other possibilities are discussed later in the text of this book. The date is interesting because it suggests that bantams were first established in this country early in the 17th century. What still remains a mystery is the origin of the bantams which came from China and Japan at a later date (eg, Pekin and Japanese); were these also the result of developments of the Jungle Fowl?. This is surely the case, but the trail is impossible to follow.

Malines Pullet

Malines Cock

Figure 0.1 A Rare Breed from Belgium

1

DEFINING BANTAMS

General Definition

Bantams belong to the Group of Galliformes which include pheasants, guinea fowl, peafowl, grouse and poultry. They are a division of the latter, being around 25 per cent of the size of the **standard bred fowl** where this exists. In many cases they are diminutive versions of the large fowl, but not always, because some are "natural bantams" and have no large equivalent.

There is recognition that the domesticated fowl came from one or more species of Jungle Fowl, possibly the Red Jungle Fowl with a preference being shown towards the species which originated from Burma. However, this is not absolutely certain and there is no way of establishing the precise origins of some of the poultry breeds because they differ quite considerably from the Red Jungle Fowl, and this applies particularly to the Malay type of birds which have physical characteristics which differ quite considerably from the 'standard' anatomy of the fowl.

Doubt has been expressed on the origins of the Brahma and Cochin breeds. These are quite different from the standard type such as Old English Game and therefore there may be some species which have passed into domestication and are not recognized because it is assumed they came from something else.

The Jungle Fowl is a very small bird being around bantam size and therefore it could be said that bantams are the **originals,** whereas the large fowl are developed species. The increased sizes came from domestication, better feeding, careful selection and related factors. However, the evolution has occurred over many centuries and this book is on the *modern* position.

We must accept the fact that the bantam is a miniature of the large fowl or a naturally small fowl. However, some fowl are small anyway so it would be a mistake to assume that smallness always equates to bantams. Silkies are prime examples where the **standard size** is 3 to 4 lb (around one kilo) and yet the Brahma male bantam is around 2 lb. and Orpingtons may be up to 36 oz. But the upper limit of the large Brahma is 12 lb. and the Buff Orpington is 10 lb. In the UK the Silkie is regarded as a light-breed **large** fowl, but in the USA the standard Silkie is a bantam only. In the UK there are now bantam Silkies.

In the past some authorities have referred to bantams as "Lilliputian Breeds" basing the connection on *Gulliver' Travels* by Jonathan Swift (1726) where one Lemuel Gulliver landed on an island where the people were six inches tall. Fortunately, the comparison is not valid because on the whole bantams are agreeable creatures and live in harmony even with large fowl, although, cheekily, the bantam cock will be on the lookout for a larger mate should the opportunity present itself. Sometimes, the poultry keeper who is lax in his penning of birds, suddenly finds he has bred some

Campines   Rumpless   Frizzles

Faverolles

Group of Jungle Fowl; Red at bottom

Yokohamas

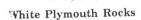 White Plymouth Rocks

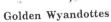 Golden Wyandottes

 Dark Dorkings

Figure 1.1 The Jungle Fowl & Some of the Many
breeds from this Species

medium size birds when he was expecting large fowl.

The Weights

As noted, the weights of bantams is usually regarded as **25 per cent** (a quarter) of the standard size. This guide is an **approximation** and on analysis it will be found that there are variations of this standard. For example, if Old English Game bantams are taken, with a standard weight of 18 to 26 oz. the large Game is 5 to 6 lb (80 to 96 oz.) it will be seen that the proportion does not work out exactly as indicated. A useful exercise is to take the standard weights for the different breeds and work out the proportion.

Earlier writers looked upon **20** per cent as the standard size compared with the large *standard*. W F Entwisle writing in 1890 (*Bantams* published 1892) stated this was the rule – one fifth of the standard size. There have been many changes since then and, although the permitted weight has changed upwards, bantams are more natural; they are no longer dwarfs (implying a certain loss of gracefulness), but are diminutive, well proportioned birds, which are beautiful as well as small.

Research has shown that the percentage may vary from around 19 per cent for Cochins and over 28 per cent for Leghorns and Indian Game. There is a dwarfing gene which can produce the bantamized fowl and when it emerges from large fowl the small bird can be bred back to the parent and the offspring then selected until the bantam finally emerges. As a boy, in the local farmyard, I well remember the small Game bantams that strutted around and, even when the larger bird was put in the yard, it seemed that the offspring were

RED MALAYS
                              WHITE POLAND HEN   GOLD POLANDS
PARTRIDGE COCHINS   WHITE COCHINS

**Figure 1.2 Some Early Bantams from Entwisle's
Breeding**

quickly bantamized, no doubt due to the vigour of the
bantam cockerels.

According to Entwisle (ibid) the best way of bantamizing birds was to select bantams with similar features to those being bantamized and then by selection
breed the desired form. Thus in the case of Brahma
bantams he states that after a number of experiments:

1. **Grey Aseel Cock X Cochin hens small in size**
2. **Grey Aseel Cock X Yellow Legged White Booted
Bantams**
3. **Produce from 1 and 2 mated together; but this
produced very disappointing results.**
4. **Light Brahma Cock (large fowl but on small
side) X Pullets from 3. Tails were too long and
they were too large. However, the Aseel cock
gave the correct type of comb.**
5. **Light Brahma cockerel X Japanese Bantam
Hens. This gave the small size, but unsuitable
combs and tails.**
6. **Light Brahma cockerel X Japanese bantam
cross (5). This cross produced winners, but there
were still difficulties with tails.**
7. **Continued to use the original cross (excluding
Japanese) and by selection produced Brahma
bantams from these. They did not have the problem tails.**

This is a summary of the crosses and results. It
indicates how much effort has to go into producing bantams from large fowl. Today there are many more
breeds in bantam form, so the problems would not be as
great as in those pioneering days, more that a century
ago.

BRAHMA BANTAMS
DARK COCK.   DARK HEN.   PAIR OF LIGHT BRAHMAS

Figure 1.3 Brahma Bantams

From *Bantams* by W F Entwisle (see text)

The reference to **standard weight** refers to normal fowl which are correctly fed. Any birds which are too fat or thin and emaciated could not be regarded as normal. In viewing birds for size the carriage and conformation would also be considered. A bantam with longer legs than normal or with a large head or other non-standard feature would disqualify anyway so the question of weight would not arise.

In viewing different breeds it must be appreciated that overall visual size is no guide to weight because some breeds are very fluffy in feathering (eg, Pekins and Orpingtons) whereas others are tight feathered (eg, Old English Game, Modern Game and Indian Game). The difference in structure must be considered when examining birds.

Are Bantams Exact Miniatures of Large Fowl?

The answer depends on the breed. Some are almost exact models of the equivalent large fowl; others are quite near, but differ in some way simply because the breeder has not yet achieved the target. Even today there are some breeds that do not have bantams. There are also some (the natural bantams) which do not have the equivalent in large fowl.

For each breed there are different varieties (usually variations in colour) and these are not standardized in different countries so expect to see some colours in the *American Standards of Perfection* which are not in the *British Poutry Standards* and vice versa.

In the early days the new bantams tended to have smaller, rounder heads than the large fowl of the same breed. Also their walk tended to be different, more

Figure 1.4 Comparison of OEG large and Bantams
Note the difference in the tail and overall carriage. The USA
bantam conforms more to the large Game.

stilted. These differences still exist to some degree, but they vary from one breed to another. As the breeders' skills have improved the bantams have also developed to a greater degree of perfection.

They still tend to have a jaunty manner and are quick in movement.

How Did Bantams Originate?

The early writers have stated that the original name 'Bantam' came from the name of a place (***Bantam*** in Java). These early birds were the equivalent of the Rosecomb. The Java fowl (large and bantam) recognized in the USA is a different breed and has a single comb. The American Java bantams are of recent origin, being recognized in 1960.

Many writers have stated that this is folk lore, not based on fact, because many small breeds of poultry existed in many parts of Asia*.

The word Bantam may be derived from the words 'Banty' or 'Bantling', used to denote a small child, rather under nourished, but this is only supposition*.

The fact remains that 'bantam' is now part of the English language to mean something small and diminutive; in a sense, it also implies a form of endearment, because a bantam is usually looked upon as a pet rather than an objective of commerce. Whilst large fowl may be regarded in the same way by some fanciers, this is not to the same extent.

---

* *See* **Sir Edward Brown,** *Poultry Breeding & Production*, **London, 1929.**

As noted earlier, the Jungle Fowl is a diminutive fowl (the definition of the bantam) and therefore the claim that bantams are of recent origin is a statement to be challenged. Quite likely there were bantams around before the large fowl and these would be what we now regard as the true bantams; ie, not reduced down from large fowl.

Development of the Present–Day Bantams

The reference therefore must be to the modern-type of bantam. The original (natural) have been recognized and acknowledged for centuries* and, if we count that Entwisle *(ibid)* was the originator of many of the 'man-made' bantams (miniatures of large fowl), they were "made" around 1860.

An American source gives further evidence. Wm M Lewis in *The People's Practical Poultry Book,* 3rd Ed 1871, states:

> *Pekin or Cochin*: This most remarkable of all the numerous bantams was first introduced in England in 1862 or 1863 and one or two pairs have been shown in this country. It is said the original progenitors were stolen from the Summer Palace, at Pekin.

At that time the author mentions other bantams in existence:

> 1. Sebrights; 2. Black Bantams; 3. White Bantams; 4. Japanese Bantams; 5. Black Java; 6. Silkies, which are regarded as bantams by the Americans. They were known as early as the 13th century !*

* See *Bantam Breeding & Genetics,* Fred P Jeffrey, where he quotes Leonora Hering , a poultry historian, as stating that the Silkie was mentioned by Marco Polo (*The Book,* 1298-99) as well as Aldrovandi and Gesner at later dates.

This American book is of great historical importance because it shows Old English Game bantams at a time when most of the writers in Britain were stating that "Game" meant Modern Game and not OEG bantams. More is stated on this subject in later chapters.*

Yet, as demonstrated by the author, OEG bantams had been in existence for a considerable period, not in the later refined state which came in the 1850s, but nevertheless, as part of the rural scenes of Britain, strutting the farmyards and small holdings of those who wished to keep that particular type of hardy, small fowl*. OEG came before Modern Game which were purely show birds.

Possible Sources of Bantams

Turning back to the question of the origin of bantams we have the following possible sources:

1. Natural bantams which, as far as we know, were always small. Japanese, Pekins Belgian, and Nankins are examples.

2. Man-created bantams, with no large equivalent, the best known being the Sebright, - Gold and Silver varieties - created by Sir John Sebright, Bart, in the late 18th century or early 19th century. There is some doubt on the exact date - as would be expected from a breed that was evolved over many years from crossing different breeds.

3. Bantams which are bred down from the equivalent large fowl by using other bantams and then by selection gradually creating the correct type (would take many years). W F Entwisle is the father of the Bantam Movement and was responsible for many new breeds and varieties.

* See also : *Old English Game Bantams,* J Batty, where the history of Modern Game and OEG is covered more fully. A drawing by Harrison Weir reproduced in the Preliminaries of this book also proves the early existence of OEG bantams.

4. Bantams which appeared as 'Sports' from the large fowl and then matched back to gradually produce a smaller race. This does not appear to have been used very much to originate bantams, but is adopted quite extensively to obtain new varieties such as a new colour which suddenly appears or a new feature such as a tassel or crest which is 'fixed' by breeding and selection.

As noted earlier, the chance of breeding an unusual type is always present. This comes from a bantamizing gene or an unstable colour gene and. once present, can be used to create others by breeding back to the original parents or related stock. It is a practice followed regularly in aviculture to breed new varieties of Parrakeets of which the budgerigar, starting from the normal Green has produced dozens of new varieties as well as a different shape and sizes.

In bantams, Old English Game breed has a large number of colours and other breeds have also many colours, whereas others continue with one colour only; eg, Ancona.

THE GROWTH OF THE BANTAM FANCY

From the Victorian era, when the large fowl was the dominant interest, the bantam has gradually replaced it in numbers so that at poultry shows they are much more in evidence than their larger counterparts. It is interesting to consider why this has occurred. The possible reasons are as follows:

1. The rapid growth of the poultry industry from the 1920s which led to the development of large scale poultry units and special, commercial type birds (hybrids) to maximize results.

This development may have outgrown its usefulness and (hopefully) with the swing back to free range poultry farming the standard breeds will return, although there is no suggestion that these will replace the bantams kept by fanciers.

2. Bantams take up less space and eat a smaller amount of food. Many of them lay fewer eggs than large fowl and they are smaller, but the fancier does not seem to mind these facts.

3. They become very tame and are kept as pets suitable for children.

4. For preparing for shows and transporting there, they are much more manageable than large fowl, which are four times the size.

5. A greater variety and many more breeds can be kept in a relatively small space.

6. Bantams are small, attractive and often quite beautiful.

7. For schools and similar establishments wishing to study biology, zoology, incubation, and genetics they are easy to keep.

8. Generally, after the first few weeks (when extra care is needed with the chicks hatched) they are quite strong and generally trouble free.

9. Bantams kept at the bottom of a garden - even running on a lawn - do not do any significant damage, whereas large fowl, must have much more space and their scratching can be harmful.

10. For the fancier who wins top prizes the stock fetches high prices and if he or she wishes there is plenty of activity at poultry shows and in judging.

Keeping bantams is very much the realm of the hobbyist, although there are a few bantam-poultry farmers who manage to make a profit from the activity. The aim usually is to enjoy keeping and breeding birds which are useful as well as attractive. The ultimate aim is to win prizes at shows and thereby improve the bantams kept. Each year, by improving the stock by careful and skilful breeding, the fancier derives great satisfaction from his hobby.

LINK WITH LARGE FOWL

As noted, although the large standard bred fowl have declined in numbers, it is necessary to emphasize that those bantams which are produced from reducing the size of the large fowl should come as near as possible to the originals. Generally speaking, there should be no departure from the *standards* laid down for the large fowl, except for size.

As will be shown later this is not always the case. For example, the bantam version of Old English Game in its British form has now departed considarably from the large OEG which it originally followed. There are others also where deviations have occurred. Not all varieties* (mainly different colours) are the same in the large and bantam; in some breeds there are more colours in the large fowl than the bantam and vice versa.

Where large fowl do exist and there is no equivalent, natural bantam (eg, the Cochin and Pekin which are separate breeds in Britain), then there should be no

*A *variety* is a sub-species within a *breed* - usually a different colour. Thus we have a large number of varieties in Old English Game, mainly colours, but there are sub-varieties such as Muffs, Hennies and Tassels. Although it is usually stated that *type makes the breed , colour and markings the variety,* this is very much a simplification because some breeds are determined by colour; eg, Ancona, where there is only one colour, and, as noted, other features may determine the variety; eg, type of comb where single and rose comb is found. Thus in Rhode Island Reds and Anconas both combs are permitted which constitutes a different variety. A *breed* must be capable of breeding true.

question of trying to breed bantams which depart widely from the large fowl; otherwise the time will come when the bantam is a distinct and different type.

If this does occur the Clubs concerned should ensure that the **standards** are modified and birds judged accordingly. For example, the continued lip service to Oxford Game Club *standards* for bantams is quite wrong; Herbert Atkinson a leader of the Club had little time for bantams as Game fowl, so why this adherence to this false standard for so many years? The practice is also misleading to the new fancier who is told to follow a standard which the judges do not use for judging; this is bound to discourage newcomers to the Fancy.

Genetics

In recent years a great deal of attention has been paid to the science of genetics. A number of scientists and poultry breeders have made a study of the fowl – its colours and other characteristics – even stipulating specific genes for main attributes.

A fancier with knowledge of genetics is able to understand what he is trying to achieve to breed the standard **type** for his or her breed. Unfortunately, the precise make–up of individual birds is unknown and therefore we can never be sure what will emerge from a particular breeding pen. This is why a fancier who has found the correct combination tends to inbreed and thus 'fix' the characteristics. At the same time, the skilful breeder knows when he must introduce new and related blood to maintain vigour. Any success must stem from breeding skills rather than scientific knowledge *on its own*, and fanciers must (and usually do) acknowledge this fact.

2

CLASSIFICATION

General Classification

Poultry have been classified in a variety of ways, and much of this was the work of Sir Edward Brown (*Races of Domestic Poultry*) who did not concern himself with bantams, which were regarded as being of little importance at that time.

Bantams began to be taken seriously around 1920 and from then on the number of breeds multiplied. If we include natural bantams the *Classification,* based on modern ideas would be as follows:

Natural Bantams
Belgian
Barbu d'Anvers
Barbu d'uccle
Booted
Dutch or Old Dutch Bantam
Japanese
Nankin
Pekin
Rosecomb
Sebright (this in not necessarily a 'natural' bantam in its own right, because it was evolved from other breeds)
Tuzo

Ornamental Bantams

As above for 'Natural' Bantams and the following:

Brahma, Frizzle, Poland (Polish)

Others may be added from time to time; eg, Araucana is a possibility. There is also the category of **'true bantams'** when a breed has been established so long that it reproduces quite faithfully as a bantam and may be significantly different from the large breed.

According to Country of Origin

(THE CLASS OF FOWL)

American

Ameraucanas*+

Catalanas*+

Chanticleer

Cubalayas*+

Delawares*+

Dominique* in USA

Fayoumi Bantams+ (based on Egyptian large breed)

Hollands*+

Jersey Giant* in USA

Lamonas*+

New Hampshire Red*

Plymouth Rock*

Rhode Island Red*

Sumatra Game* in USA

Wyandotte*

Asiatic

Aseel (also spelt Asil)*

Black Sumatra*

Brahma*

---

* Denotes bantam as well as large fowl;

+ Exists in USA, but not in Britain.

Cochin (In bantams is the Pekin)
Frizzle*
Java*
Langshan: Croad and Modern*
Malay*
Phoenix*
Shamo*
Silkie (In USA is bantam and 'bantam Silkies have been developed in Britain))
Yokohama*

Belgian
Braekel
Campine* in USA
Malines

British
Australorp*
Dorking*
Hamburgh*
Indian Game*
Marsh Daisy
Modern Game*
Norfolk Grey
Old English Game*
Old English Pheasant Fowl
Orpington*
Redcap* in USA
Scots Dumpy*

* Denotes bantam as well as large fowl;
+ Exists in USA, but not in Britain.

Scots Grey*
Sussex*

Chile
Araucana* : normal and rumpless

Dutch
Barnevelder*
Friesland
North Holland Blue
Welsummer*

French
Bresse
Creve-coeur*
Faverolles*
Houdan*
La Fleche*
Mantes
Marans*

German
Bearded Thuringians
German Bantams
Kraienkoppe*
Lakenvelder* in USA
Vorwerk

Hungarian
Transylvanian Naked Neck

---

* Denotes bantam as well as large fowl.
+ Exists in USA, but not in Britain.

Italian
Ancona*
Leghorn*
Sicilian Buttercup

Polish
Poland***

Russian
Orloff*

Spanish
Andalusian*
Minorca*
Spanish*

Switzerland
Appenzeller*+ in USA

***Not all agree this came from Poland, the 'Poll' being re-garded as the crest.
* Denotes bantam as well as large fowl;
+ Exists in USA, but not in Britain.

CLASS DIVIDED INTO BREEDS SUB-DIVIDED INTO
VARIETIES

The classification shown above is the fundamental breakdown. In addition, the breeds have characteristics which are listed in the official poultry *standards*. These form the basis for comparison and judging. The latter consists of comparing the individual bird with the *standard* and then assessing the relative merits of each bird in a class at the show. Those coming nearest to the *standard* and being fit and healthy are chosen as the prize winners.

Economic Qualities Classification

Breeds may be classified on the basis of how they perform in economic terms and this is as follows:

1. **Layers (usually non-sitters); eg, Leghorns and Anconas.**
2. **Table birds; eg, Indian Game**
3. **Dual or General Purpose breeds; eg, Dorking, Sussex and Old English Game.**

For bantams, which are primarily show birds, this classification does not have the same significance as for large fowl. Although bantams are eaten, the commercial value is relatively small. However, it does give an indication of the type of fowl being dealt with. If a table bird in the large fowl the bantam would be expected to show similar characteristics.

The fact remains that bantams can be worthwhile for eating and for laying purposes. They are economic in the amount they eat so the food conversion ratio can be incredibly high in terms of eggs or meat.

On the utility side the following may be regarded as excellent 'all-rounders'; if they are a little over standard weight this does not matter because the smaller birds can be selected for the show.

Examples of a choice selection would be:

Buff Plymouth Rocks (Males 26 to 30 oz. / 740 to 850 g.; Hens 22 to 26 oz.)

Light Sussex   (Males 40 oz.; Females 28 oz ; ie, 1130 and 790 g. respectively)

Rhode Island Reds (Males 28 to 32 oz. ; Females 24 to 28 oz.)

Wyandottes (Males 24 to 28 oz. Females 20 to 24 oz.)

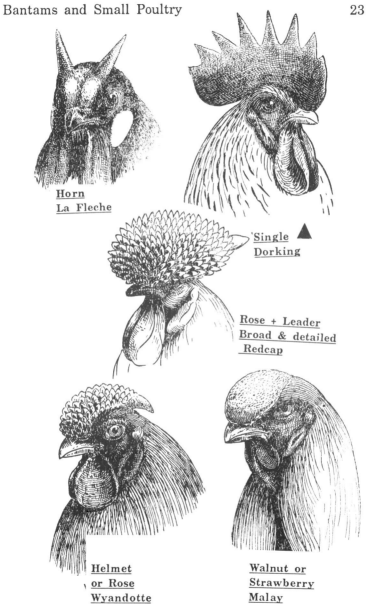

Horn
La Fleche

'Single
Dorking

Rose + Leader
Broad & detailed
Redcap

Helmet
or Rose
Wyandotte

Walnut or
Strawberry
Malay

Figure 2.1 Diverse Types of Comb
Also see page 37.

Other Characteristics
Other means of differentiating breeds are as follows:
1. Body shape and carriage
This is a fundamental breed determinant and is a vital importance. Birds which are not of the correct shape cannot comply with the standard and therefore have no recognizable identity.
2. Colour of feathers
Whether 'hard' or 'soft' feathered; colours and characteriotioo of foathoro, all dotcrminc thc varicty within the breed.
3. Colour of Legs (and Feet) and Number of Toes and whether spurred; feathered legs.
Legs are generally coloured on the basis of the plumage, the white birds having white shanks and the darker ones having dark colours. Usually the number of toes is four, but some breeds have an extra toe. Some breeds have feathered legs.
4. Type of Comb, Ear Lobes & Beards, Crests or Muffs.
A wide range of combs exist and a breed usually has a specific comb type; with some breeds there may be a single **or** a rose comb, although the two types do not mix in the same pen of fowl; ie, one or the other would be allowed, but not either so one tends to emerge as dominant. Thus Rhode Island Reds may have a single or rose comb, but single is the norm. **Ear lobes** may be round, oval or other shape, and colours differ. Crests and other embellishments may cover the head and face.
5. Colour of Flesh
For table birds there are definite preferences in the colour of the flesh, white being preferred in Britain, but

Ancona

Andalusian

Araucana
(Lavender)

Aseel
(Spangle)

Australorp

Barnevelder
(Double Laced)

Charles Francis

Rumpless Bantam

Pekin Bantams
(See also Cochins)

Frizzle Bantam
(Blue)

Japanese Bantams
(Greys)

Old English Game Bantams

Gold Sebrights

(Black Red: English type;
See large Game for USA)

Rectangle

Circle

Rhode Island Red   Wyandotte

Gravy Bowl
Shape

Egg
Shape

Plymouth Rock   Leghorn

Figure 2.2 Shapes which determine the Type

important in some breeds, such as Indian Game and Wyandottes, so the feeding should encourage this colour.

6. Type of Tail

Tails differ enormously and without the correct tail the character is lost. There is usually a specific standard angle as well as the type of feathers.

6. Colour of Egg Shell

Many large fowl lay brown eggs. The bantams such as Barnevelders, Marans and Welsummers should lay very dark brown eggs, but in the early strains of these bantam breeds the brown egg factor was lost. This was due to using bantams which laid white or tinted eggs to reduce the size. Some are still the wrong colour.

HARD FEATHERED & SOFT FEATHERED

The breeder has to decide whether to keep **soft** feathered or **hard feathered** birds. The Poultry Club defines 'soft feathered ' as those breeds which do not come into the hard–feathered group which consists of the Game breeds such as Old English Game, Modern Game, Indian Game, Aseel, Malay, Shamo, Thai Game and Sumatra Game. The group has tended to enlarge in recent years, especially with the interest in Asian–type fowl.

The soft feathered bantams have a profusion of feathers and generally need more attention for showing. They must be fed fairly high protein layers' pellets and protected from extremes of weather.

The hard feathered group have tight, glossy feathers and will generally manage with mixed corn and greens. Also they must have plenty of exercise to

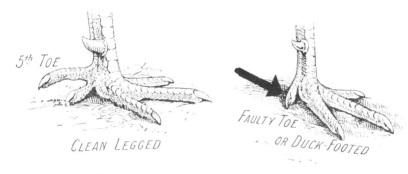

Five toed Breed
Dorkings, Faverolles
& Silkie

Duck-footed
Avoid, esp. in
Game breeds.

Full Feather Leg

Vulture Hocks
Unacceptable
for most breeds
except Sultan

Figure 2.3 Examples of Leg Types

Legs (& feet) may be mottled, feathered, coloured, or varied
in some other way; some have light feathering only.

develop their muscles and make them fit. At the same time, it must be appreciated that hard feathered bantams must have protein to maintain feathers or these will become very brittle and break. All too often OEG bantams are seen at the summer shows with broken feathers and lack of sheen; yet with the introduction of layers' pellets for one meal this can be avoided.

A More Sophisticated Classification Essential

The division into 'soft' and 'hard' feathered birds is too broad in its approach. There is no difficulty with the hard feathered breeds – all Game breeds of some type, but the so-called **soft-feathered Group** is a mixture of breeds which vary tremendously in type and therefore some further breakdown is vital.

We cannot really talk sensibly of breeds such as the Leghorn and Brahma, suggesting they are similar by grouping them together. Moreover, the type of feathering is not the only variation.

A more logical approach,when analysing by feather structure, would be to group the breeds along the following lines:

1. Tight or Close Feathering (the equivalent of the Hard Feathered)

2. Medium Feathering
The Mediterranean breeds and others which are similar would come into this category.

3. Profuse or Loose Feathering
The Asian breeds such as the Brahmas and Cochins would come under this heading.

The advantage of this approach would be a more accurate description of the type of feathering and the nature of the breed.

OEG

Modern Game

Malays

Indian Game

Figure 2.5 Hard Feathered Breeds

All carry the feathers close to the body and are Game in
character. Include Sumatra, Aseel, Shamo, Tuzo and others.

The Mediterranean Breeds

The breeds which come under this heading have specific features. They are more like OEG in appearance than they are the soft–feathered Asiatic breeds (Remember Malays and other Game birds are also Asian in origin) and it seems quite wrong to group them with a group so different. They have characteristics which separate them from the Game as will be apparent:

1. They are non sitters

Over centuries the natural instinct to become broody and rear chicks has disappeared from the Mediterranean Breeds. This has come about from a variety of reasons, possibly:

(a) selection of birds which do not come broody and therefore maximize egg production; some believe this may be due to the Roman Catholic religion which allowed the use of eggs on fast days when meat was forbidden;

(b) extensive use of artificial incubators in Egypt from early times, which discouraged broodiness in the hens and was, therefore, bred out of them.

2. Sprightly and Active in Carriage

The Mediterranean breeds are active, for ever on the move, taking in the necessary food, grit and water for producing a large quantity of large, white eggs.

3. The Comb structure is Single and follows a Pattern

In the male bird the comb is large and upright with positive serrations and the female has a comb which droops or folds on one side.

Spanish   Campine

Scots Grey   Booted

Figure 2.4 Medium Feathered Breeds

These come between the truly hard feathered and soft
feathered breeds so an extended classification is desirable.

4. Feathering is Abundant and Tails are Carried High

This feature makes them quite different from the breeds such as the Brahma. The feathering is fairly tight, but not as tight as the Game breeds - hence the suggestion that they should be classified as 'Medium Feathered'.

5. Body Shape is Long and Oval Indicating Laying Qualities

The Mediterranean Breeds

These consist of the Ancona, Andalusian, Leghorn, Minorca and Spanish. They come from the shores of the Mediterranean.

Original location in itself is not the only requirement for a Mediterrannean breed. There may be others which have originated from adjacent area eg, Sicilian Buttercups, but do not have exactly the same characteristics.

Others may be cosmopolitan breeds which may have some M-B characteristics, which came from a cross with one of them, or the breed may have developed quite independently. An examination of the various breeds, even at a most superficial level, will indicate that many come within the **'medium' category.** Thus examples are:

Bresse (French), Campine (Belgian), Hamburgh (British, but note with Rose comb), Lakenvelder (Germany), Norfolk Grey (British) and Scots Grey (Scottish).

3

THE BREEDS I

There now follows a description of the breeds found in bantam form. These are shown in alphabetical order, but this is only for ease of reference. *For more detail on specific aspects the reader is advised to study the breed <u>standards.</u>*

Where possible the descriptions have been simplified and this has meant omitting some of the features. It is hoped that the text plus the illustrations will guide the reader on the essentials.

As noted earlier, in referring to the development of the breeds of bantams which have been produced from large fowl, there must be acknowledgement of the type and nature of the specific large breed. This has involved looking at the history of some of these.

Method of Approach

In listing defects the obvious ones for the breed are given. Where these are likely to be common to all birds they have not been repeated, but must be taken into account when judging **any** bantams. They include:

Injuries, Illness; deformities such as roach or crooked back, lameness, wrong number ot toes, duck-footedness, squirrel-tail; wry-tail, mis-shapen and sprigs or marks on comb, split wing, twisted hackles, leg faults, beak crossed or mis-formed; any other feature not in a normal, healthy bird of the type being considered.

ANCONA

Type: Layer, Light breed.

Origin: Miniature of Mediterranean breed; from Ancona in Italy.

Size: British Type; Male 20 to 24 oz. (570 to 680g.) Female 18 to 22 oz. **USA:** Cocks 26 oz

Hard or Soft Feathered: Soft (although feathers not as fluffy or abundant as heavy breeds)

Comb: British Type: single or rose; single comb upright in cock, falling to one side in hen with 5 to 7 even serrations. **USA:** single comb.

Tail: Carried at a 40⁰ angle and full. USA tends to be fuller.

Legs, Feet : Clean; yellow with black mottles; USA Yellow.

Beak & Eyes: Yellow mixed with black or horn colour. **Eyes**: Orange red **(USA = Reddish Bay)** with hazel pupils.

Description: Mediterranean-type shape of body, small compact. White, almond-shaped ear lobes.

Colour: Feathers which are greeny-black in colour and each tipped with a V-shaped "spangles" or Mottles, as evenly distributed as possible. The tip should be neat and distinct, but not so obvious as to make the fowl a mottled variety as the mottled Leghorn.

Characteristics: Very active and tends to be alert and 'flighty'. Non-sitters.

Show Qualities: Strong support from club, but numbers not as large as in earlier days. Very attractive breed.

Production Qualities: Table poor; laying some strains very good, but show requirements can affect produc-

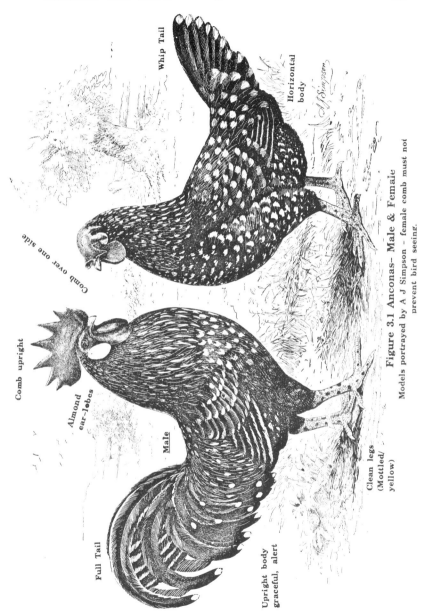

Whip Tail

Horizontal body

A J Simpson

Comb over one side

Comb upright

Almond ear-lobes

Male

Full Tail

Upright body graceful, alert

Clean legs (Mottled/ yellow)

Figure 3.1 Anconas– Male & Female

Models portrayed by A J Simpson – female comb must not prevent bird seeing.

tiviity, breeding for mottles and colour not best criteria for laying.

Exhibition Faults: Faults in colour which should be black to roots (difficult to achieve). Lack of tips or tips indistinct. White in face. Not to type. Deformity of any kind.

Special Notes: Have been in existence and shown since the 1920s. Recognized in Britain from that time. In USA standards from 1960.

As noted, some strains are excellent layers.

Plumage must be bottle green/black with a positive sheen. Breeding should be from stock which is black to the roots and never from birds which are blue/black.

Double mating used to be common practice for breeding prize winning cocks or pullets:

(a) **Cockerel breeding:** Use hens which tend to have small combs without excessive fold.

(b) **Pullet breeding:** Use cock with large, slender combs.

In this way each pen breeds the type that is required for showing. This practise is frowned upon by some because they argue that the standard should not require double mating.

This is a breed recommended for garden poultry keeping, but a net or wire netting cover should be on the run, otherwise the birds may fly over. For showing they need to be tamed by constant contact and by show pen training.

Existence of Tips: Since the existence of clearly defined tips is of the utmost importance, it follows that any serious breeding programme needs to aim to im-

Figure 3.2 Mediterranean–Type Comb
Ancona, Andalusian, Leghorn and Minorca Types

prove this characteristic. This aspect is worth 20 points and will go a long way towards producing a winner. Therefore *avoid* birds in the breeding pen which have the following:

(a) **Crescent shaped spangles or a broad, irregular shape, or lacing;**

(b) **Lack of colour in tips or green-black;**

(c) **Poor flight feathers;**

(d) **Tail which is not black to the roots;**

(e) **Legs which are not mottled.**

The aim is to breed from those which have the correct markings and also ample reserve of the green-black colour pigment.

The Rose Combed Ancona

The Rose Comb variety is not the original version and probably came from crossing with the Spangled Hamburgh or the Silver Laced Wyandotte. It continues to exist, but not usually in bantams in the UK.

A perfect specimen
is difficult to
achieve

Figure 3.3 The Tip of the Ancona Feather

*Readers requiring more detail on this breed are referred to *Understanding Pure Breeds of Poultry : Anconas*, J Batty.

ANDALUSIAN

Type: Layer, light breed.

Origin: From Spanish large breed.

Size: Male: 24 to 28 oz. Female 20 to 24 oz.

Hard or Soft Feathered: Soft, but not too abundant.

Comb: Single with the female having one fold to one side of the head, but not covering the eye.

Tail: Upright with long feathers and carried at an angle of 40^0.

Legs & Feet: Longish and without feathering on shanks. Dark slate or black.

Beak & Eyes: Horn or dark slate. **Eyes:** Reddish bay.

Description: Mediterranean–type body, compact, but taller than Anconas; resemble Minorcas, but the face is smooth and bright red in colour (not blood red as in Minorca) and *fair* size, white ear lobes, almond shaped and flat.

Colour: Blue only. This is a grey slate colour and the body feathers are laced with black. Colour of hackle and back on cock is a darker shade described in the standard as 'black', but is often a deep–purple slate colour resembling black. In the USA standard the head is given as Black and other references are to **Bluish Slate.**

Characteristics: Racy, handsome birds; more stable than Anconas.

Show Qualities: Very attractive. Present no serious problems, except not all chicks will be blue.

Production Qualities: Poor table birds, but respectable layers. Breeding problems when breeding Blue X Blue; will produce 50% Blue and the remainder Black and Black and White Splashed in equal numbers.

Comb deeply serrated.
(following line of neck)

Body
long; breast
full, not too
rounded.

Male

Eyes dark red
Almond ear lobes

Comb single
fold to one side
(should not cover
eye)

Long deep
body

Legs dark

Female

Figure 3.4 Andalusians
Note: Taller than Ancona;legs dark slate or black.

Exhibition Faults: Red in lobes, white on face, white in plumage, rusty hackles, faulty comb, faulty tail, and legs of the wrong colour.

Special Notes: It is not essential for double mating, although this has been attempted in the past to obtain better combs in males. However, some breeders do suggest that heavily laced birds should be used for pullet breeding because there is a tendency to lose colour. If the cock is light the hens should be dark or use black and white splashed together and then select the correct blue colour. Once a sound colour is achieved, with correct selection of hens (*some* with upright combs to get the correct combs for males) the problems are avoided.

This is an old breed in large fowl and has been around since the 1850s.

Entwisle mentioned Andalusian bantams in his book (*Bantams*) published in 1884 after his death two years earlier. He compiled a *standard* for the breed.

My experience of breeding Blue Andalusians is very limited. My father was quite keen on them many years ago. However, as regards breeding Blue Fowl (Old English Game) my experience extends over a considerable period and what difficulties there are in trying to achieve the correct shade of colour! Some come black or almost black, others are splashed, some are white, and a few are a sound grey-blue. However, it seems that some strains have been produced from blues other than those of a Black origin (possibly a certain strain of Blue Game) and these may produce more consistent Blues.

This concept is certainly worthy of development, because the so-called 'Andalusian Blue' creates many problems in colour being a diffusion of black and white and difficult to stabilize. The ground colour is given 30 points and the lacing 20 so a great deal of attention must be given to this aspect.

Because of these difficulties it seems that this breed, despite its attractiveness, is destined to continue to be low in numbers. The aim should be to get a clear blue ground-colour without a sooty colour on the breast and on the throat. Combining the lacing and the correct colour requires great care in breeding.

The American Andalusian follows the British type, yet the Ancona, Leghorn, and Minorca in the American style have longer, fuller tails, set at a lower angle. They follow the same form as the Sicilian Buttercup, which is also from the Mediterannean area. There is a suspician that a cross was made with a long-tailed fowl, thus giving the great development at the base of the tail of the breeds mentioned. The original Leghorns, illustrated in many sources, do not have this extra long tail. Some have suggested that the difference in climate has caused the difference, but this seems unlikely. In any event, the Andalusians and Spanish would have also developed in the same way, which has not occurred.

APPENZELLER

This is a Swiss breed which is quite ancient and used to be kept in Yorkshire under the name of 'Hornet'[*]. It is similar in head points to La Fleche and has the horned comb, but V-shaped. The crest is upright and forward, rather like a crew cut..

The breed was brought back to this country and has made a remarkable recovery in large fowl. Bantams do exist, but have not been plentiful in Britain. In the USA there are three colours: Black, Golden Spangled and Silver Spangled.

The full name is the *Appenzeller Spitzhauben*. There is also a near relative the *Appenzeller Barthuhner* which has a rose comb, and which is heavier in weight. The colours are Partridge, Blue and Black. This is also known as the Appenzeller Bearded and is regarded as a German breed by some authorities, although this is not absolutely clear.

[*] *The Encycloepedia of Poultry*, Hicks J S., c. 1920. Also *The Appenzeller*, Ken Speaks, Poultry Club Year Book, 1994.

Appenzeller (Silver)
Male

Small comb
+ small crest
+ muffs.

Araucanas

Figure 3.5 Appenzeller & Araucanas.

ARAUCANAS*+

Type: Light breed; layers of blue/green eggs
Origin: Chile; some variation in types
Size: Male 26 to 30 oz. (750 to 850g.) Female 24 to 28 oz.
Hard or Soft Feathered: Soft feathered.
Comb: Very small. Head has a top knot, crest, or muffs. The terminology is confusing and the Araucana possesses a combined coverage of the head and face.
Tail: Standard suggests 'well developed', but this is a relative term and compared with the earlier breeds (Ancona and Andalusian) would be regarded as medium. It is carried at an angle of 45^0, but is not tall.
Legs & Feet: Medium, but look short in the female. Legs variable in colour; can be olive, slate or willow.
Beak & Eyes: To match legs and eyes to be orange red.
Description: Long, deep body, with head higher than tip of tail. Carriage horizontal.
Colour: Various colours following the OEG main colour pattern with lavender as a favourite. Black reds, brown–reds, duckwing, pile, and cuckoo are all permissible.
Characteristics: An active fowl with wide variety to interest the fancier who wants something different.
Show Qualities: An unusual breed which attracts attention. I recall seeing these in Scotland long before they appeared in England.

---

*In the USA the breed is different from standard type in the UK. The USA breed has ear tufts, but no crest and looks similar to a blue-eared pheasant without a tail. They have also created an Ameraucana which is a modified Araucana.
+ Apparently known originally as Araucuna; see Encycloepedia of Poultry, Hicks J S, c. 1920.

Production Qualities: A dual purpose fowl with reasonable laying ability and with a plump breast for a table bird. The blue or green egg is a novelty, but there is no extra commercial value in this fact unless it can be exploited.

Exhibition Faults: Lacking full breast; no muffs or crest, but when present must *not* be the same as the Poland crest; comb other than Pea-type; large comb in female; daw or light eye; feathers on legs; wrong colours in body or legs; exhibiting a high tail or low wings.

Special Notes: This is a breed which has not yet been standardized into a final form. It seems to come in many varieties and the main common factor is the blue coloured egg.

RUMPLESS ARAUCANA

This has been recognized in the USA since 1976. It is more recently recognized in Britain. As noted earlier it resembles an eared pheasant, minus its tail. Although claimed to be a variation of the tailed Araucana at present there seems some doubt. The two breeds do not even look alike; the rumpless has a graceful curved neck and a low wing carriage which is different from the normal, tailed type.

BANTAMS TO FOLLOW LARGE FOWL

The bantam must follow the large fowl in type and must be relatively small because the large version should not exceed 7.lb in the mature male (UK) and only 5 lb in the USA. This makes the bantam a maximum of 26 oz. (USA). In UK weights are 24 oz. to 30 oz., ie, 680 to 850g., the male being larger.

ASEEL

Type: Light breed, but sitters.

Origin: From India where it was used for cockfighting; the bantam is a miniature of the fighting breed. According to Entwisle these were bred in the 1850s and formed the foundation for bantams in Indian Game and Malays.

Size: The large Aseel are around 5 to 6 lb, but in recent years some very large birds have appeared in the Birmingham area which are reputedly Aseel, but we wonder if these are crossed with Malays, although there is no proof either way. Bantams should be 25% of the large; British Poultry Standards suggest 40 oz for males and 32 oz for hens. This appears too large, especially when Entwisle (*Bantams,* p 34) had Aseel bantams at 18 to 22 oz. in the 1890s.

Hard or Soft Feathered: Hard feathered/close feathered. Feathering very sparse and tight fitting.

Comb: Pea, but no wattles or very slight.

Tail: Tends towards a whip tail, but fuller; of medium length. The position is below horizontal carried away from the body.

Legs & Feet: Strong and squarish and deep yellow in colour. Follow line of body.

Beak & Eyes: Horn or yellow with dark tint. **Eyes:** Pearl, yellow or daw. Must be 'beetle browed' (overhanging) giving fierce expression.

Description: A compact, muscular bird with a wide body, upright carriage and drooping tail.

Colour: Black–reds, greys, spangles, whites, reds and many other natural colours exist.

Broad Shouldered, whip tailed

Rose Comb
Flattish Head
No wattles

Low tail

Legs bent at hocks
Flat shanks

Very Hard Feathered

Figure 3.6 Aseel
The large and bantams should be identical in type.
A very hard feathered, pugnacious type of breed.

Characteristics: A pugnacious breed which wants to fight at all times. They are attractive, but need special attention. Even hens will fight so they are best kept in pairs.

Show Qualities: Not often seen, but do exist in a few hands.

Production Qualities: Lay a few eggs each year, rather like a wild bird laying a clutch and then wanting to sit on them. Make reasonable table birds, but slow to mature.

Exhibition Faults: Lacking character of Aseel; looking too much like Indian Game; red or dark eye; tallness; no beetle brow; rather feathery; round shanks; wrong carriage.

Special Notes: This is a breed for those who want to keep an interesting variety with a wide variety of colours. I well remember more than 20 years ago seeing Aseel bantams in Yorkshire which had been bred down from large Aseel without introducing any new blood. It had taken many years to get to size. As noted, Entwisle produced these from large fowl and they were very small. He was the first to achieve this bantamization of the Asian breeds.

In the USA the Bantam Standards recognize five varieties: Black–red, black, spangles, white, and silver.

AUSTRALORP

Type: Heavy Breed.

Origin: Bred as a utility type from the British Black Orpington (which was transformed into a feathery exhibition type); the original version which went out to Australia and remained in the true form.

Size: 36 oz (1020g maximum) in male and 28 oz (790g. max.) in female.

Hard or Soft Feathered: Soft or loose feathering, but not excessively so. The Orpington is now very feathery.

Comb: Single and not too large.

Tail: Rounded tail which follows a natural flow from the saddle; quite full, but sickle feathers not markedly separated from rest.

Legs & Feet: Clean; fairly low and black in colour.

Eyes & Beak: Eyes dark; Beak dark.

Description: A full bodied bird which is quite long, but not obviously so because the shape is roundish.

Colours: Black and Blue. Plumage should be black/green-sheen for Black and slate/blue for Blue with darker lacing. Blue cocks to be a dark colour on head, hackle, saddle back and tail.

Characteristics: A docile breed which exhibits all the sound qualities of the original dual purpose breed.

Show Qualities: Has had some success and should continue to have support. In the black no special attention is required. The blue will require selection for even colouring.

Production Qualities: Good layer; body is plump.

Exhibition Faults: White in plumage; light coloured eyes; tall or otherwise wrong shape; any deformities or

uncharacteristic features. Cross reference should be
made to **Black Orpingtons** under 'Orpingtons'.

Single comb, evenly serrated.
                              Red in face, comb and wattles.

Feathers
Green/Black
In Blues Dark
Top male, rest
laced. Females
slate-grey
laced darker.

Male

Compact body
rounded breast

Black legs

white soles

reasonable length.
(Orpingtons now
barely visible)
                                            Female

Figure 3.7 Australorps
Developed from original, utility type Black Orpington
Descriptions apply to both sexes.

BARNEVELDERS

Type: Heavy Breed; or more correctly Medium–heavy breed (according to the Dutch approach).

Origin: Holland, produced in the district of Barneveld. They came from crossing Cochins, Brahmas and Langshans, the process starting about 1850 and proceeding until 1899 when it was discovered that the breed had stabilized and a distinct breed had developed because those laying the darkest eggs had been kept to satisfy customers in the market. Thus the forces of the market had created the new breed. In 1906 they were crossed with Buff Orpingtons to produce a more partridge colour. In 1910 efforts were made to obtain uniformity and the name Barnevelder was established.*

They were given recognition in the UK in the 1920s and the bantams came in the 1930s. The main problem has been the loss of the dark brown egg factor.

Size: 32 oz.(910g.) male to 26 oz.(740g.) female, maximum.

Hard or Soft Feathered: Soft: Medium type.

Comb: Single not too high.

Tail: Conventional tail with clear sickles fairly upright.

Legs & Feet: Clean; yellow in all varieties.

Eyes & Beak: Rich bay; **Beak:** yellow.

Description: A bird with a rotund–shaped body which displays a prominent breast; legs medium;

Colour: Black, double laced, and partridge (no Silver in Bantams). The **Double-Laced** is the one generally

---

* Information based on a paper given at the World Poultry Congress held at the Crystal Palace, England in 1930. The authors were Dutch poultry experts P J Wijk and P Ubbels.

Figure 3.8 Barnevelders (Double laced)
For description of lacing and other features see text.

seen. Blacks (black all over with green sheen) are very scarce and the Partridge (similar to double laced, but more brown markings and the male a black-red type) is looked upon by some as being a mismarked laced. The **double laced** requires both male and female to be reddish brown with black lacing which is broad and distinct. With the hen the neck should be black with or without red markings. The breast should have double lacing, one inner and an outer, the latter being broad and distinct.

In the cock: each feather in the hackle should be black with a reddy-brown edging and a similar colour stem. The back should be deep red with wide black lacing. Thighs, tail and upper parts should be green-black.

Note on Standard: It was deliberately modified to avoid double mating for separate pens for male and female.

Characteristics: A hardy, alert breed with a very dark brown egg in the **large breed**, but not achieved in the bantams. Many believe this is the reason for their relative scarcity when the large fowl are quite popular.

Show Qualities: Difficult to obtain the perfect lacing required in the Double-laced variety.

Production Qualities: Reasonable layers, but continue to disappoint with the colour of the eggs.

Exhibition Faults: White lobes, mismarked lacing; feathered legs; wrong colours in plumage; legs other than yellow.

Special Notes: The dark brown egg factor took many years to achieve and is very difficult to pass on to a bantam. Once another breed was introduced to reduce the size there were problems.

BELGIAN BANTAMS++

Type: Natural bantams, classed as 'Ornamentals' and those found in the UK are:

> 1. **Barbu d'Anvers (Bearded Antwerp), which are rose combed and cleaned legged;**
> 2. **Barbu d'Uccle (Bearded Uccle), which have a single comb and are feather-legged.**
>
> **They are known as 'Bearded Bantams'.**

Origin: Belgium, although it is suggested that they may have originated from China or Burma and are depicted on a painting by Albert Cuyp (1620 – 1691).*
Modern birds come from Belgium where they have been developed into many varieties.

Size: Diminutive: 24 to 28 oz, (680g. to 790g.),but Bearded Uccle can be slightly larger.

Hard or Soft Feathered: Soft, but medium type.

Comb: As above 1 and 2. Comb, face, ear lobes, and very tiny wattles should be red.

Tail: Short at a slight angle in the Barbu d'Anvers and slightly taller and more upright in the Barbu d'Uccle. It is important to see the difference by comparing the two breeds.

Legs & Feet: Short shanks with little visible thigh. Colour varies with variety. On the Uccle the feathering must be long and inclining downwards.

Eyes & Beak: Eyes dark and vary with plumage; similarly with beak which should match legs. Beard and facial feathers form a positive shape which fits in with the flow or shape of the neck hackle. This is to re-

---

++This description is brief and the standards are difficult to follow, with many of the finer details requiring explanation from an expert in the breeds.

* Source: *Bantam Breeding & Genetics*, Fred P Jeffrey, USA

Clean legged

Barbu d'Anvers

Single comb   Taller than d'Anvers

Longer
in back

Feathered legs

Barbu d'Uccle

Figure 3.9 Belgian Bantams
Both are bearded and "bull-necked"

semble a 'bull neck' (known as a "boulle") The beard should form three ovals (a trilobe), standing well away from the head, one at each side and the other below the beak.

Description: A natural bantam which is very small, full fronted and compact. In the **d'Anvers** the head tends to be large with a curved, short beak which matches the colour of the plumage. In fact, the hen appears owl-like and unlike the male the hackle is not thick at the back.

With the **d'Uccle,** the hen does not have such a dense beard. It is short in all aspects and very cobby.

Colours: There are many colours found in both breeds, although certain colours appear to be preferred :

(a) Millfleur
Orange red with mahoghany red on the wing bows of the male. Overall an intricate pattern of black spots and white triangles.

(b) Porcelaine
A Beautiful creamy colour background ("Light Straw") with the pattern of spots in blue with white triangles.

(c) Self Blues (There are many variations in Blue)
As for other blue breeds in a pale shade. An Andalusian Blue.

(d) Cuckoo
Light grey with bars of a darker shade.

(e) Quail
A mixture of black, gold and umber with the black predominating on hackle and tail.

(f) Black Mottled
Green black with an even distribution of white tips on the feathers.

Other colours exist. In the USA there are 14 varieties (Bantam Standards) and in the UK a similar number, but there is overlap and some differences. Reference to the *Standards* is advised.

Characteristics: Attractive breeds of bantams which are quite hardy, although the feathered leg varieties (d'Uccle) are best kept in an open-fronted house, with shutters for inclement weather. They are proud and jaunty bantams which are not difficult to breed.

Show Qualities: Are purely show birds and therefore must be bred exactly to the standard type and colour description.

Exhibition Faults: Colour defects, existence of obvious wattles, prominent earlobes, wry or squirrel tail, long legs; absence of muffling or beard, wrong type of comb, feathers on legs of Antwerp.

Special Notes: Some strains lay well in Spring and Summer. They are very attractive and make ideal bantams for the dedicated show person. There is a tendency to specialize in a few colours only so, although many are listed, not all are seen at shows.

Generally there are no particular mating problems so double mating is not essential. They are suited to the expert or the beginner. The Millfleurs d'Uccle and the Porcelaine are probably the most attractive of all ornamental bantams. There is a dedicated following and Club.

WATERMAEL
(Barbu d'Watermael)

These are closely related to the Belgian bantams described. They possess unfeathered legs, a topknot, beard, and rose comb with three spikes. As yet they are not standardized in Britain or the USA.

BOOTED BANTAM (SABELPOOT)

Type: Natural bantam; quite ancient.

Origin: Posibly China or Japan. They came to Europe via Holland and are depicted in 17th century paintings. In essence they are similar to the Belgian bantams, but without the "Bull Neck". Apparently in Belgium, they were known as the Sabelpoot and this is a name being adopted by breeders in the UK at present, which is difficult to understand because the old name is well established. According to the Americans they came from Germany; the American Standard of Perfection regard the Booted as a non-bearded Belgian bantam (the Uccle without a beard), but the British *standard* prefers to regard Booted as a separate breed entirely.

Size: 20 to 26 oz. depending upon age and sex; cocks are the larger size.

Hard or Soft Feathered: Soft, but medium in density.

Comb: Single with even serrations and of medium height.

Tail: Largish with definite, long sickles; upright in male, not quite so prominent in the female.

Legs & Feet: Feathered on shanks and feet, very plentiful and stiff.

Eyes & Beak: Dark to match plumage, but in the white the eyes should be red and legs white.

Description: A quaint, natural bantam with rounded breast, very short back, tall tail, and legs which are well feathered. The face should not be muffed or bearded.

Colour: The white seems to have been the first recorded colour, being recognized in the first standards.

Spangles from around 1890

Feathered
legs
No beards

No "boulle"
or bull-neck.

White Booted Bantam Cock & Hen

Figure 3.10 Booted Bantams
Now undergoing a revival

Other colours are blacks, spangles, black mottled, millfleur and porcelaine. The black and white were the originals and we suspect that the last two colours stated are a result of crosses with Belgian bantams, which is a pity; this can only result in the *bull neck* appearing in the Booted, when this is not in character.

Characteristics: It has gone through a number of modifications, including birds which had a look of Japanese bantams with longer legs than normal. They have now settled at a more upright bird with reasonably long legs (although the standard states "fairly short") to show the feathers to advantage. **The ASP stipulates medium thighs and shanks.**

Show Qualities: Purely show bantams and therefore must be treated with care so that the feathers on the legs are not damaged.

Exhibition Faults: Resembling a Belgian bantam; foul feathering; white on earlobes; too cobby; wattles large; toes not heavily feathered.

Special Notes: According to older records this was a popular bantam, but suffered from disadvantages: **poor fertility, chicks difficult to rear, and feathering on legs, all need watching very carefully.** All these points had merit, but these days with modern feeding, with higher protein, and attention to housing, so they have broken straw or shavings on the ground, there should be no difficulty.

At one time yellow legs were in vogue, but then changed to white. Now there is a move to be as near as possible to Belgian bantams, which serves as a guide to possible colours, but not to change the character completely. Entwisle *(ibid)* had Black Booted in 1841.

BRAHMA

Type: Heavy Breed: rather majestic fowl; ornamental-type in bantams.

Origin: From Asia, but whether in the present form originally is open to question. Much controversy surrounded their appearance when they arrived in the UK and the USA* in large form. In bantams in 1890s.

Size: 38 oz.(1080g.) Male and 32 oz. Female.

Hard or Soft-Feathered: Soft with a great abundance of plumage.

Comb: Pea, curved so that it is higher in the middle. It should be noted that the Brahma has an unusual skull which is medium in length, but deep and broad with overhang, which is referred to as 'beetle brow' in hard feathered birds; ie, skull has over-hanging eye-brows.

Tail: Medium in height, gently curving from the saddle (the cushion); no obvious sickle feathers as in some breeds. Black in colour.

Legs & Feet: Feathered, colour appropriate to breed. Shanks yellow. Length long in male, shorter in female. The thighs are covered in a profusion of feathers. *Vulture hocks+* call for disqualification in the USA, but in the UK are regarded as undesirable.

Description: A majestic bird with a body which is full, deep and broad. The outer side of the legs are well feathered and this extends to the feet. The head is in proportion to the body with full hackles and surmounted by a prominent pea comb.

---

*See *The Brahma Fowl,* Lewis Wright, now out of print.
+ See page 27 for illustration.

Triple comb detail

Well developed Cushion
vital. Feathered Legs,
But best avoid vulture hocks

Well   Majestic in
feathered   Bearing

Dark

Light

Figure 3.11 Brahma Bantams

Buffs are similar to Lights, but with an with an even buff
colour instead of white. Male is larger than hen.

Colour(s): Originally Light and Dark, but now extended to White, Gold, and Buff Columbian (Buffs in USA). The colours consist of the following:

Silver Pencilled Variety

(a) Dark; Male - follow the Silver-pencilled type of plumage. Head silver white (greyish white); hackle black with lacing of silver white; body black; back, saddle, wing bows and wing bays silver white.

(b) Dark; Female - Head silver white; Overall grey in colour with even, silver white pencilling on each feather.

Columbian Varieties

(a) Light; Male - White (or other colour) with black markings on hackle (stripes) and on tail coverts.

(b) Dark; Female - Body white (or other self colour) with neck striped with black; tail striped with black; foot feathers striped with black.

The Buff Columbian comes into this category, substituting 'buff' for white.

*Partridge Variety**

(a) Male; Gold - Although called a Gold it appears to very much resemble the Partridge variety so well known in Wyandottes is a bird which is 'rich gold' in colour with breast and tail black. The leg feathers are also black.

(b) Gold - Female - same basic colour of rich gold with neck hackles striped with black; body feathers finely pencilled with black; tail black.

---

* The British *standard* calls this Gold, but in reality the bird is a partridge colour, except the colour is Gold and not red or orange-red. It is useful to compare the *standard* for the Partridge type in Cochins and Pekins.

Colour (cont.)
White: The colour must be self white throughout in both sexes.
Characteristics: A dual purpose breed which could be counted upon for eggs and meat. The large fowl are not as prolific as in earlier times. The bantams lay well and make excellent mothers.
Show Qualities: Exotic birds, tall and majestic. Since the colour is worth 30 points and and type and carriage 35 points it follows that colour and type must be correct or the birds will not win top awards.
Show Faults: Departure from prescribed colour; wrong type of comb; too small; little or no leg feathers; foul feathering; lacking characteristic, majestic carriage.
Special Notes: This breed is no longer as popular as years ago, but it does have a following – hence the introduction of the new colours, other than Dark and Light. All kinds of claims were made for the breed and it was given fancy names.
With some of the colours it seems that double mating is essential to obtain the perfect colours, but this is being overcome by careful selection. With Darks the *solid* black breast is not the type to produce fine lacing in the females. Lights were also double mated to bring out the dark hackle stripes.
One of the main problems has been to get the appearance of a Brahma – majestic carriage and bearing in a smaller bird, yet still give the impression of being a heavy breed. Entwisle (ibid) was breeding these in the 1880s. The approach adopted is explained in Chapter 1.

BRESSE

Type: Light breed, yet a good table bird.
Origin: France.
Size: Up to 36 oz., but not standardized.
Hard or Soft-Feathered: Soft, but like the Mediterranean breeds.
Comb: Single
Description: Rather like the Leghorn, but with better table properties.
Colour(s): Black and White.
Special Notes: Not developed as a popular breed in the UK or the USA and seems unlikely to be taken up as a bantam.

Figure 3.12 Bresse

BLACK
LA BRESSE.

BRAEKEL, BREDA, AND BUCKEYE

These are recognized in the USA , but not in the UK.

CAMPINE

Type: Light weight which is very attractive.
Origin: Belgium
Size: Mature birds 22 oz hen and 26 oz. cocks.
Hard or Soft-Feathered: Soft, but close feathered.
Comb: Medium size and single, with the female drooping to one side.
Tail: The male is "hen-feathered" which means there are no positive sickle feathers. It also means that the plumuge in both sexes is similar. Carried at a 45° angle (40 degrees for female).
Legs & Feet: Long legs (thigh and shanks) ; **colour:** leaden blue.
Description: A racy looking bird, with tight feathering. Rounded and broad at the front with a short back; fairly upright with a 'game' look about the cock.
Colour(s): Two colours; Gold and Silver. Consists of hackle feathers (called the *cape* as for Game fowl) of a distinct colour (Rich Gold or Silver-white according to variety) and then bars of a beetle green colour imposed on the main, **ground colour** of gold or white.
Characteristics: A sprightly and attractive bird with unusual barring which should be **three times** the width of the ground colour. This is known as autosomal barring. Difficult to reproduce if introducing outside blood, eg, OEG bantam to get size right.
Production Qualities: Are good layers and table birds as large, but bantam qualities unknown.
Exhibition Qualities: Extremely attractive, and would certainly be given top awards if of quality. Both Gold and Silver have been shown at national level, but remain very scarce.

Show Faults: Tail feathers not 'Henny' type; incorrect width of barring; lack of front; pencilling or other defect on ground colour; faulty comb; eyes other than dark brown; wrong colour legs, beak and toe nails; feathers on legs; any deformity.

Special Notes: In Britain the Campine bantam is very rarely seen, but is attractive enough for more followers to take them up. Even in the USA they are scarce. Rex Woods felt they had a future as bantams, if only for their fondness for human company*.

Cock 'Hen Feathered' ie, same feathering as hen.
Tail no distinct curved sickles.

Figure 3.13 Campine Male

*The Poultry Fancier: an article - Some of Our Bantams are Missing. (June, 1968, no longer published)

CATALINAS

A **Mediterranean-type bantam.** Buff in colour and attractive, it comes from Spain and its full title is *Catalina Del Prat Leonada.* Although primarily an egg-laying breed like the others from that area the large fowl is regarded as a dual purpose breed.

CHANTECLER

A Canadian breed which is very hardy. The overall shape tends to be that of Indian (Cornish) Game, but much more feathery, rather like a Wyandotte. Both these breeds appear in its make up, together with the Leghorn and Rhode Island Red. The colours are Partridge and White, but are scarce in the USA and not standardized in Britain.

Figure 3.14
Creve Coeur
Described later, attractive, but not often seen in bantams.

Figure 3.15 Cochin   USA type
Tend to be taller than the British Pekins

COCHIN (Pekin in UK)

The name **Cochin** has now been discarded by the bantam fanciers in the UK on the grounds that the bantam is a breed which is quite distinct from the large varieties. In the USA the **large breed** is acknowledged to be derived from the Chinese Shangai Fowl which arrived in the USA and England around 1845. Entwisle gives the date for bantams as 1860/61. The British position is covered under "Pekins" the name preferred in the UK.

Type: Heavy breed with abundant feathering.

Origin: Asia: from China.

Size: 34 to 38 oz. (male heavier)

Hard or Soft-Feathered: Soft.

Comb: Single.

Legs & Feet: Feathered.

Description: Massive birds in large fowl so large in bantams; full, round figure with considerable feathering; lower in stature than the Brahma.

Colour(s): There are 16 varieties found in the USA and they are extremely popular. **Colours are:** Barred, Birchen, Black, Black Tailed Red, Blue, Brown Red, Buff, Buff Columbian, Columbian, Golden Laced, Mottled, Partridge, Red, Silver Laced, Silver Pencilled, and White.

Characteristics: Shaped like a ball, with very heavy feathering, these are gentle and easy to keep, except they should not be let out in conditions which would spoil the mass of feathering, especially on the legs and feet.

Show Qualities: Ideal for showing, but legs must receive special attention.

Show Faults: Shape and colour and lack of type **(See Pekins)**

CORNISH (USA)
(Known as Indian Game in Britain)

In the USA there are ten colours recognized by the Bantam Association. They are Black, Blue, Blue Laced Red, Buff, Columbian, Dark, Mottled, Spangled, White and White Laced Red. In the USA the name Indian Game was dropped in favour of Cornish Game as long ago as 1920.

CREEPER

This is a short legged fowl which is described as very similar to a Dorking, but with even shorter legs. Possibly a bantamized Scots Dumpy fits the bill. They are found rarely, but known colours are Black, White, Silver and Cuckoo. They are not standardized in Britain.
See the entries for Scots Dumpies *and* German Bantams

CREVE COEUR

This is a French breed which has a crest, muffs, a beard and an unusual shaped comb – V–shaped. In bantam form it is rarely seen. It is similar to the Houdan.

Figure 3.16 Comb of Creve Coeur
This is very unusual

CROAD LANGSHAN

Type: An Asiatic breed in its large form, it takes its prefix from its first importer a Major Croad. A heavy breed with lightly feathered legs and the layer of brown eggs.
Origin: China.
Size: Males 27 to 32 oz. (770 to 910g.); females 23 to 28 oz. (650 to 790g.). In the USA weights are 4oz. heavier.
Hard or Soft Feathered: Soft, tending to be 'loose' compared with some breeds, but not as feathery as Brahmas or Cochins.
Comb: Single with five or six spikes and of medium height. Wattles in proportion.
Tail: High with abundant feathers and two main sickle feathers showing quite distinctly. Cock's tail 75 degree angle and female 70 degrees.
Legs & Feet: Medium length with feathers down side and on outer toe, but must not be heavy or vulture hocked. Not to be tall standing like Modern Langshans, which appear to be the type favoured in the USA. Shanks to be Bluish Black with web and bottom of feet pinkish white without black spots. On the shanks pink/red should show between scales. Toe nails white.
Beak & Eyes: Curved and reasonably long; Horn colour in Blacks. In the USA there is a White variety with lighter colouring. **Eyes:** Dark Brown.
Description: A tall majestic breed with shortish neck, long broad body, with full breast, and quite short back in the male; the wings are carried high – almost 'goosewinged'.

Colours: Dense black with beetle-green sheen, quite brilliant. White variety: pure white.

Characteristics: A large, utility type bird which should be clear from its appearance.

Show Qualities: Large, showy type which always looks well in a show pen.

Production Qualities: Intended to be a dual purpose fowl with a tendency towards a table bird.

Exhibition Faults: Wrong colour legs (usual fault yellow); legs or outer toe lacking in feathers; black soles on feet; vulture hocks; yellowish face or beak; foul feathering, including purple or much white in Blacks; yellow skin; wrong carriage; small tail or wrong angle.

Special Notes: An interesting breed which has appeared many times in reasonable numbers. A little white may appear in the foot feathers which is said to indicate the right blood. They are in existence at the present time, stock having been imported from Germany.

MODERN LANGSHAN

This breed does not appear as a bantam. If it is created it should be taller than the *Croad* with a whip tail and tight feathering.

Figure 3.17 Croad Langshans

CUBALAYA

As the name indicates this breed originates from Cuba. In some respects it resembles the long–tailed Japanese Fowl, but is thought to have Asian Game blood as well. In the USA there are Blacks, Whites, and Dark Reds. They are not standardized in Britain.

DELAWARE (USA)

This is a barred bantam, known as a "Columbian-type" because of the marking which is rather like a Light Sussex. In the USA it has been recognized since 1960.

DOMINIQUE

Type: A medium weight American Fowl which in its large form was developed for meat and eggs. It was known as the 'Hawk-coloured Fowl' because of its resemblance to that bird.

Origin: The ABA standards suggest a combination of Hamburgh and Asiatic, but this may not be the case because they have a long history, possibly pre-dating the importation of the Asian breeds of Brahma and Cochin.

They were standardized in 1874, but were in existence prior to that date, being illustrated in the third edition of *The People's Practical Poultry Book*, Wm M Lewis in 1871. Bantams have only been recognized in the Standards since 1960 in the USA and are not usually seen in Britain. They were in existence long before they were standardized.

Size: In weight they are 7lb. for the cock and 5lb. for the hen. Bantams are 28 and 24oz. for male and female respectively.

Hard or Soft-Feathered: Although soft feathered the feathers fit close to the body and follow the traditional pattern of a farmyard fowl.

Comb: Rose which is moderately wide with the point turning slightly upwards.

Tail: Long and quite full carried at a 45^0 angle.

Legs & Feet: Clean legged which are medium in length and with four toes. The skin and legs are yellow.

Description: Body broad with a full breast and wings strong and full. Carriage fairly upright. Being dual purpose they are expected to be active and productive.

Figure 3.18 Example of Dominiques
Now quite rare they are worthy of revival

Colour(s): With a slate under-colour the overall impression is fairly sombre, but attractive. The main colour is slate on a whitish background. The earlier writers referred to this colour as 'slatey blue' shading. Each feather has a dark tip and the bars are irregular in width.

Characteristics: A barred breed, which is quite attractive.

Show Qualities: Rarely seen, even in the USA. Used to 'make' other barred breeds.

Production Qualities: In large fowl a dual purpose breed, but not enough bantams around to judge. Yellow skin; eggs brown.

Exhibition Qualities: Attractive with imperfect bar–
ring and rose comb.
Show Faults: Wrong colour in plumage, particularly
yellow or red.

White Dorkings   (Note rose comb on White)

Figure 3.19 Dorkings: Style to Aim for in Bantams
Silver Grey (bottom) main colour, but Whites possible

DORKING

Type: This breed is one of the oldest known as a standard breed, being found or brought by the Romans in the first century AD. At one time it was regarded as the finest of fowl, combining table and egg laying qualities. Around 1830 it had a fairly upright carriage, but subsequently this became low and horizontal,* possibly influenced by a cross with the Scots Dumpy. A characteristic is the possession of five toes.

In bantams it has always been rare and those that appear are not typical of the large breed.

Origin: British, but somewhat changed over the years because of various introductions of new blood.

Size: Standards suggest: In Britain 30 to 48 oz, (910 to 1360g.), the cocks being the larger weights. In the USA they are smaller with a top recommended weight of 32 to 36 oz.

Hard or Soft Feathered: Soft. Well feathered.

Comb: Medium in size. Single, but in certain varieties rose. Wattles and ear lobes red and of a good length.

Tail: Thick and well spread and carried at an angle of 35° (hen) and 45 (cock)

Legs & Feet: *Standards:* Legs Medium (USA) and short in UK; five toed, white, and no feathers. Thighs not greatly visible because of profusion of feathers.

Eyes & Beak: Full eyes, but not protruding; beak well set, medium and slightly curved.

Description: Large bodied and deep, and when viewed sideways forming a square. Longish, broad back.

---

* For a full description see *Sussex & Dorking Fowl,* J **Batty.**

Colour: In the USA there are Grey (also known as 'Coloured' or 'Dark'); Cuckoo; Silver Grey, and White; these may be rose comb in Cuckoo, Grey and White and single or rose comb in the Silver Grey. In the UK bantams are rarely seen and then usually in Silver Grey.

The Silver Grey cock should be pure in colour with silver hackle and shoulders and black breast (rather like a Silver Duckwing); the matching hen should have a grey body with 'partridge' markings, a salmon breast and neck hackles silvery white with a black stripe.

Characteristics: Bird with a horizontal carriage of square to oblong shape (from side); stately and placid in nature.

Show Qualities: Could do well because it is now purely a show breed, but lack of numbers make progress very difficult.

Production Qualities: Would make a good dual purpose breed; cocks up to 48 oz. (1360g) make it a heavy bantam.

Exhibition Faults: Wrong shape – many bantams too upright; lacking fifth toe; wrong colour (eg, white in black breast); wrong type of comb; long legs; bumble feet or twisted toes; lacking breed characteristics.

Special Notes: This is a breed worth cultivating because it has great potential. Sadly, despite efforts from the Club, very little advance has been made. The same report applies to the USA.

There are a few around, usually appearing at national shows. But the position appears to have deteriorated. In 1913 A J Major kept them and a breeder, R Scott Miller, was advertising five colours which originated from the Major strain. They also appeared in 1955 and later dates, but always in very low numbers from one or two exhibitors only.

DUTCH

(Also known as Old Dutch Bantams)

Type: Similar to Rosecomb in having a full breast and well developed tail. A natural bantam.

Origin: Holland; an ancient breed.

Size: Small; 14 to 20 oz. female (400 to 570g.); 510 to 680 oz. male (510 to 680g.)

Hard or Soft Feathered: Soft, but feathers tightly wrapped around body, almost Game-like.

Comb: Single of moderate size; USA specify 5 spikes. Ear lobes moderate, of kid-like quality and white.

Tail: Full with well developed, curved sickles on cock; full tail, spread, on hen.

Legs & Feet: Clean of moderate length, tending to shortness, four toes.

Eyes & Beak: Large eyes and moderate beak.

Description: A jaunty, attractive bantam which is now well established. Follows the Jungle Fowl stamp in shape and carriage.

Colour: Many colours; Partridge, Duckwings (silver, gold and blue), Salmon. In the USA there are ten varieties.

Characteristics: Friendly birds, but tend to be aggressive in conduct with other birds, rather like Old English Game. Jaunty and alert with no serious breeding problems.

Show Qualities: Excellent show birds with brilliant feathering.

Production Qualities: Moderate layers.

Exhibition Faults: Red or poor quality in other respects in ear lobes; white in face; lack of tail; defective

comb; poor colour; weak hackle; very drooping wings.
Special Notes: The main colours (USA) are Black,
Blue, Black-Red, Blue-Red, Cuckoo, Golden, White,
Wheaten. These should comply with the standard col-
our patterns usually associated with OEG bantams.
Mismarkings or foul feathering should be penalized.
In the USA there are also **Dutch Bearded** and **Dutch
Owlbeard.**

Figure 3.20 Dutch Bantams
Very attractive with bright colours

FAVEROLLES

Also known as Faverolle, but addition of 's' is more accurate because it follows place name.

Type: Heavy breed, with a thick body and longish back, but with beard or muffs and feathered legs.

Origin: French, from village of Faverolles; possibly related to the British Dorking.

Size: 32 oz (910 g) for female, rising up to 48 oz. (1360 g.) for the developed male. The USA standard specifies 24 to 30 oz, so a much smaller bird is expected.

Hard or Soft Feathered: Soft with fairly abundant feathering.

Comb: Single, conventional with four to six serrations.

Tail: Carried at 45 degrees for male and 40 for female. There are differences of opinion on length of tail; British standard suggests moderately long, but this is misleading because it tends to be moderate; ie, medium, although fairly upright.

Legs & Feet: White; lightly feathered on outer shanks, with an extra toe at the back.

Eyes & Beak: Prominent eyes; head broad and short with full beard (mufflings). Small ear lobes (hidden).

Description: A majestic dual purpose bird, yet active. Not as deep in keel as Dorking and more leg showing.

Colours: Black, Blue, Salmon, Ermine, Buff, White. and Cuckoo.

Characteristics: Quite tame and friendly.

Show Qualities: Great potential, but the leg feathering and beard do present a challenge. Covered runs advisable with adequate clean litter.

Production Qualities: The utility aspects are stressed for show birds.

Single comb

Beard

Full breast
Deep Keel

Feathered
Legs (outer)

Small comb

Very long
Body

Horizontal
carriage

Faverolles Hen

Figure 3.21 Faverolles
Five-toed breed

Exhibition Faults: Any feature not characteristic of a heavy breed; skin or legs other than white; no feathering on legs; absence of fifth toe; lack of muffling; coarse comb; not a miniature of large fowl.

Special Notes: Since 1956 the breed has tended to appear in relatively small numbers, but increasing. All colours seem to have been produced and very attractive they are. In recent years have appeared or reappeared: Whites (1960), Black (1965) Blues (1973), Buffs (1971), Cuckoo (1979) Salmon and Ermine were bred earlier.*

The main features of the colours are:

Black. Blue, White and **Buff** – self colours which follow the normal pattern expected for any popular breeds; Blues are a darkish shade with slightly darker lacing, and Buffs should be a **deep, even** buff colour.

Salmon: *Male:* Straw coloured neck and saddle hackle; shoulders and back salmon (cherry mahogany); remainder black, including leg feathering and muffs.

Female: Body wheaten brown with a dark striping in the hackle; breast and lower body a cream colour.

Ermine: Follows the **columbian**-colour-pattern of the Light Sussex and Wyandotte of that name.

Cuckoo: are a barred breed and the colour is similar to other breeds.

*For a full explanation see *The Faverolles*, John Kraft, in the *Poultry Club Year Book,* 1995.

FAYOUMI BANTAM

Based on the Egyptian large fowl of that name there are four different colours: Gold, Silver, (like the Pencilled Hamburghs) and Black–tailed Buff and Black–tailed White. They are attractive birds, evolved in the USA.

FRISIAN (Friesian)

Type: Active, small bantams, along the lines of the Dutch Bantam in carriage and shape. However, they are miniatures of the large breed of that name. Some believe the small size was obtained by crossing with a Sebright.

Origin: Holland. May be closely related to the Friesland fowl, but this is not clear.

Size: Around the same size as the Dutch bantam.

Hard or Soft Feathered: Soft.

Comb: Single, five points and medium in size. Almond-shaped white ear lobes.

Tail: Full with curved sickles carried at 50 degrees for male and 45 for female.

Legs & Feet: Clean shanks, moderate (visible) thighs and four toes.

Eyes & Beak: Bold and bright with strong beak.

Description: An active, attractive bantam, following Rosecomb lines, without the large earlobes or tail of the latter.

Colour: Black, Golden Pencilled and Silver Pencilled.

Characteristics: Similar to German Friesian breed and is jaunty and worth keeping for attractiveness.

Show Qualities: Excellent potential.

Exhibition Faults: Loose feathering; short legs; low wings; wrong type of comb; narrow breast; poor tail; very short body.

Special Notes: Probably related to the Hamburghs and should be of that stamp. Pencilled varieties similar to Hamburghs. Bantams not in existence in UK.

Japanese Bantam Frizzles

Figure 3.22 Frizzles
Feathers curl wrong way

FRIZZLES

Type: Rotund bodied fowl, large and bantams, which have curled feathers in place of the conventional, straight feathers. However, they appear to be a distinct species as bantams. Early illustrations show bantams in their own right. Heavy breed classification.

Origin: Asia possibly Japan or China.

Size: British standards 20 to 28 oz. (570 to 790 g): USA allows for cocks to go up to 30 oz.

Hard or Soft Feathered: Soft, but feathers curl the wrong way.

Comb: Single.

Tail: British standard stipulates that tail should be large, full and erect, but in practice this does not seem to be the case. Modern birds have moderate tails much lower than the line of the head.

Legs & Feet: Medium with very little, if any, of thigh showing. Clean legged in Britain, but in the USA there are feathered legged types, rather like the Pekin.

Eyes & Beak: Eyes full and beak fairly short.

Description: A small bird with distinctive feather growth, each one to be curled towards the head, and in an even fashion.

Colour: Many colours, including Columbian, Selfs (black, blue, buff, white) and many of the OEG colours (Black–Red, Pile, Spangle, etc.) and Rhode–Island–Red type Dark Reds. Many beautiful 'off colours' have been bred and these are quite extraordinary.

Characteristics: An active breed which may be quite a good layer, certainly the large fowl are greatly under-rated for utility qualities.

Show Qualities: Excellent show birds, but heterozygous (consisting of 'mixed' genes so do not breed true) and therefore there are many rejects when selecting show specimens. Show types crossed together produce very curly plumage which would be too extreme for exhibition. In fact, in such progeny the feathers are brittle and would not last; the cross may even be lethal.* Curl of feathers is usually given 25 points out of 100, but, since this is the main characteristic, a bird with bottor friaalo will tond to win, ovon if it hao othcr faults.

Production Qualities: Reasonable layers; good in some strains.

Exhibition Faults: Very narrow feathers, lack of curl or uneven curl; tail without curl or long; white in ear lobes; wrong colours in Selfs; feathered legs in cleaned leg variety.

Special Notes: Frizzle has been produced in other breeds, notably Japanese, Rhode Island Red and Poland. These tend to be a curiosity rather than a genuine variety.

Figure 3.23 Early Frizzle (Ludlow, c. 1850s)

* *Genetics & Evolution of the Domestic Fowl*, Stevens L, Cambridge, 1991.

Brahma
(Dark)

Belgian Bantams

(Barbu d'Uccles: Millefleur)

Campine
(Silver)

Cochins (Partridge)
For British *Bantams* see Pekins

Croad Langshan

Dorking
(Dark)

Silkie
(Blue)

Welsummer

Yokohama
(Black Red)

Wyandotte
(Gold Laced)

Modern Game
(Pile Cock & Hen;
Partridge Hen)

Old English Game
(Large Brown Reds;
USA Bantams)

GERMAN BANTAMS

There are many breeds of German bantams, many of which are similar to breeds found in other countries. These are additional to the well known Kraienkoppe, Lakenvelder and Thuringian (Thuringer) Bearded fowls. There is also a German Creeper which is similar to the Scots Dumpy. These breeds are very interesting, but do not appear to have become etablished outside Germany. Creepers have many breeding problems.

Jeffrey* mentions the 'German Bantam' with ten distinct varieties, rather like Old English Game, but having a longer body and tail. He also lists the Reichshuhner which is similar to the Rhode Island Red.

There is also an old breed Courtes-Pattes, which originated on the European continent, very similar to the Scots Dumpy, although not as heavy.

Hen

Cock

Figure 3.24 German Creeper Bantams
Also known as the Courtes-Pattes

*Fred P Jeffrey, *Bantam Breeding & Genetics*.

HAMBURGH (also HAMBURG)

Type: A racy, active breed which tends to follow the Mediterranean shape, but with many differences in characteristics. Light breed with white eggs.

Origin: Uncertain. Some suggest Dutch, but it has been bred in England from very early times.

Size: Medium; bantam 22 to 28 oz. (620 to 790 g.) USA slightly smaller.

Hard or Soft Feathered: Soft, but more correctly *medium*.

Comb: Rose rose with tapering end which continues in a straight line or goes upwards slightly. The whole to be covered in fine serrations or points, but not coarse or large. (This is a very important feature). White ear lobes to be of a good size and round and smooth.

Tail: Tall and full at an angle of 40 degrees for male and 35 for female. Well furnished with sickles and hangers. Male Laced has lacing on edge; Spangled has spangles at end (See colours below)

Legs & Feet: Clean, medium long in thighs and shanks. Four toes. Colour leaden blue.

Eyes & Beak: Eyes bright and full; beak, medium with curve.

Description: A gamey looking bird with very attractive colours in all varieties, conforming to the orthodox Jungle Fowl type of body.

Colours: Black, Pencilled, and Spangled. The pencilled and spangled are further divided into Silver and Gold. Blacks, which are similar to Back Rosecombs, are not a standard colour in bantams in the UK, but are in the USA, where White also exists.

<u>Silver Pencilled</u>
Hen has fine barring on body; cock lacing on tail, but self
coloured body (except for slight markings – see text).

<u>Gold Pencilled</u>
Cock lovely golden coloured body, lacing on tail; hen barred.

Figure 3.25 Pencilled Hamburghs

Silver Spangled Hamburghs
Note cock has Spangles (cf. with laced varieties).
Hen also fully Spangled.

Figure 3.25 Spangling on Hamburghs

Characteristics: Non–sitting fowl, once renowned for its laying qualities as a large fowl. Very active, graceful bird, with symmetrical body lines and carriage.
Show Qualities: Top rate show birds, but many exhibitors have found difficulty in getting the correct markings in the Spangled. Ear lobes and comb also difficult to get exactly correct.   When judged they are

awarded most of the points for comb, ear lobes, colour and for markings (60 points in British standard).

Production Qualities: Reasonable layers, but primarily ornamental.

Exhibition Faults: Wrong type of comb; indistinct or poor markings; ear lobes other than enamel white; squirrel or drooping tail; faulty legs and feet.

Special Notes: The markings are of vital importance in bantams and therefore must receive much attention.

Colours: (Applies to Spangles & Pencilled)

Gold Ground Colour: a rich, bright golden bay or mahogany.

Silver Ground Colour: Silver white.

Markings: Gold: Tail, stripes, spangles and tips all a green/black. **Silver:** Each feather with spangle of green black, (Spangles) or bars of green/black (Pencilled).

Note: The markings are quite precise so reference should be made to the illustrations of feathers.

Spangles: These must be round and on the end of each feather. Those which are V-shaped and run into the shaft of the feather should be discouraged.

Pencilling: This is really fine *barring* which should be even. This is caused by an autosomal barring gene and is dominant. Tails should be laced. In the cock the body is a Golden Bay or Orange-red (but Silver colour in Silver Pencilled) and on the wing coverts the upper web is black, and the lower web is pencilled with black. The underparts are also Gold, slightly pencilled with black.

The overall impression of the cock is of a beautiful, orange-red colour, with the wing bar edged with black, and slight black markings below the wing bay.

Special Notes (cont) The breed was always difficult because the large fowl, with the complex markings, could only be produced by double mating and, there was a further problem of hen feathering in the cocks. The most popular bantam variety appears to be Silver Spangled, but Silver Pencilled are also being bred.

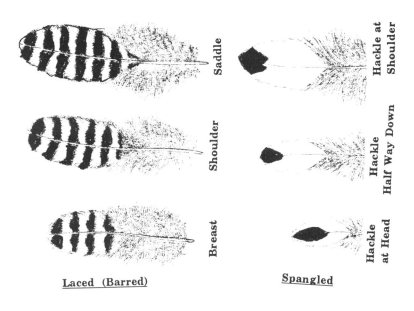

<u>Laced (Barred)</u>   <u>Spangled</u>

Figure 3.24   <u>Female</u> Feathers of Hamburghs

**Rose comb
showing fine
workings &
pointed leader**

**Ear lobes
must be
enamel
white &
round**

**Wattles rounded
& smooth**

**Figure 3.28 Style of Head & Comb of Rosecomb &
Hamburgh Bantams**

HOLLANDS

This is a breed which is recognized in the USA standards, but not British. They were produced in America from Dutch stock crossed with Leghorns, Rhode Island Reds and others. Colours are Barred and White.

HOUDAN

Type: A long bodied fowl with crest and beard and, for good measure, five toes. Originally classified as a heavy breed in Britain it is now a light breed.

Origin: France, one of the oldest breeds in large fowl.

Size: Britain 22 to 28 oz. (620 to 790 g.). The USA standard is 26 to 34 oz, the cock being the larger weight.

Hard or Soft Feathered: Soft, but not very fluffy like the Brahma or Cochin.

Comb: V- Shaped – Leaf or Butterfly (small). Face muffled or bearded, covering face. Crest large and full, quite rounded and without overhang or split..

Tail: Long and well arched; female inclined to be fanned.The angle is around 50 degrees for male and 45 for female.

Legs & Feet: Clean legged, spotted, but with five toes.

Beak & Eyes: Eyes: Beak Medium length with slight curve. **Eyes:** Prominent and red in colour.

Description: A multi–character bird, combining many unusual features on comb, crest, beard and five toes, as well as mottled plumage in the original form.

Colour: Mottled – the overall colour to be greeny black with mottles (splashes or tips) covering the body. The older birds become lighter and show more mottles. In the USA there is also a White variety.

Characteristics: Active fowls which are good layers as well as reaching a worthwhile weight.

Show Qualities: Attractive breed, but have never been popular. A number of attempts have been made to 'make' them, but the large crest and butterfly comb are deterrents. They were revived in the second world war

Figure 3.29 Houdans
A utility breed worth cultivating.

(as utility birds) and imported to the USA in 1949, and admitted to the USA standards in 1960.

Production Qualities: Commendable layers and acceptable table birds for a bantam.

Exhibition Faults: Feathered legs; faulty crest; wrong type comb; foul feathering; lacking fifth toe; any defects.

Special Notes: For many fanciers the Houdan is something of an oddity which is a great pity because it is an attractive and useful breed. Some years ago a friend, W A T Morecombe, bred large and bantams and took top show awards.

Figure 3.30 Houdan Head
This shows the unusual head and comb.

INDIAN GAME

Known as 'Cornish' in the USA

Type: A heavy weight breed which was originally bred for cockfighting by the Cornish miners and then by selection became extremely heavy boned and compact.

Origin: British, bantams are miniatures of large.

Size: Males 4.5 lb max.. (2Kilos); females 3.5 lb.. (1.60 K.). In the USA the Cornish are lighter.

Hard or Soft Feathered: Hard. with tight plumage.

Comb: Pea not too large.

Tail: Short with a leaning backwards just below horizontal.

Legs & Feet: Thick set, four toes, yellow in colour as deep as possible.

Beak: Thick and Strong. **Eyes:** Bold and a light colour, usually yellow; they should not be dark or red. The strong, broad head and overhanging eyebrows (beetle brows) are an essential feature of the breed.

Description: A thickset breed, which has a body which slopes downwards; moreover, in body shape both male and female are the same.

Colour: Darks, Jubilee and Blue Laced.

Characteristics: A friendly, slow moving bird, which is inhibited in some respects by its tendency to become more 'compact' and thickset. Fortunately, bantams, being from a cross with other breeds, tend to avoid the excesses of some of the large varieties.

Show Qualities: Now purely show birds; moderate layer, but good table birds.

Production Qualities: Table birds for those who wish to make use of the birds culled.

Figure 3.28 *Top*: Indian Game cock & Jubilee
Hens: *Bottom*: Jubilee cock & dark cock.
The Jubilee is white with red markings

Exhibition Faults: Smallness; roach back; defective lacing; leg defects; single or other incorrect comb; high tail or lack of tail; wrong colour eyes; purple comb; incorrect colours.

Special Notes: Bantams tend to be more round in the body than the large counterpart. Nevertheless, they should be judged on similar lines.

Colours:

The **Dark** males are predominantly black birds with a green sheen; wing bays are chestnut and this colour may also appear at the base of the hackle and across the back, but dense green/black bodies seem to be preferred. The female is deep chestnut brown with double lacing on feathers in a glossy green/black and a dark hackle.

Jubilee: Instead of black for male and dark chestnut for female the background colour is white. The lacing, wing bay and shoulders are a deep red colour, sometimes called bay or mahogany.

Blue Laced: Background is blue, but the same markings; a new variety in the UK (See *Cornish* entry).

Classification: Although called 'Game' the breed is not classified as Game in the same way as Old English or Modern and therefore must not appear in a Game class.

IXWORTH

Allied to Indian Game is the Ixworth breed, named after a village of that name in Suffolk, England. It looks very similar to the Indian, but has a higher tail and carriage. In Britain there used to be a bantam developed by the originator of the breed, Reginald Appleyard of duck fame. Sadly it died out with his passing.

JAPANESE BANTAMS

Type: Short-legged dwarf fowl (coming into the category of 'Creepers' which have certain characteristics, discussed below), with a low carriage and upright squirrel tail. Wings touch ground. Natural bantams.

Origin: Japan where they are known as *Chabos*. Originally they are believed to originate from China.

Size: Small:14/18 oz to 18/22 oz (400/510 to 510/620 g.) for male and female respectively.

Hard or Soft Feathered: Soft, quite feathery.

Comb: Single, very large, with four or five points, surmounted on large head, following line of neck. Large wattles.

Tail: Very tall, with high sickle feathers well above line of head (one third above head).

Legs & Feet: Legs very short, **and thick**, with no feathers; feet barely visible; bird walks with faultering gait or waddle. They are yellow in colour.

Beak: Strong and curved; yellow in colour. **Eyes:** Orange or red.

Description: A cobby, dwarf-like bantam, with high tail and large comb, low to the ground, and with prominent breast. They are to be found in normal feathering as well as *Frizzles* and *Silkies.*

Colours: These are numerous and there are many variations depending on the club concerned, eg; USA standards or British. Some are self explanatory:

> **Black Tailed White; Black tailed Buff; Buff Columbian; (see description of Columbian Wyandotte, but replacing buff for white); White; Black; Birchen Grey; Silver Grey; Dark Grey; Miller's Grey; Black Mottled;**

Blue Mottled; Red Mottled; Self Blue; Lavender Blue; Cuckoo. Red; Tri-Coloured; Black Red; Brown red; Blue Red; Duckwing and some 'off-colours'.

Characteristics: A cobby bird with a variety of features which make up its basic characteristics; short back; large tail; short legs; tiny body, and drooping wings.

Show Qualities: Purely an exhibition breed, but very difficult to breed all the required features in the individual bird. Best birds appear to be 'cut away' at the base, with wings, breast and legs all submerged into the shade.

Production Qualities: No value, except as show birds.

Exhibition Faults: Any uncharacteristic feature such as short tail, long legs, long back, faulty comb, wings set high, **lobes** which are white, any other fault not consistent with a dwarf bantam.

Special Notes: Japanese are for dedicated show people; they present a serious challenge and there are many colours. Because they are what is known as a "creeper" type there are many breeding problems. Even if fertility is satisfactory the *short leg X short leg* is a lethal gene and this results in chicks dying in the shell, usually around the 18th day. Yet the correct procedure for breeding is to mate short leg with short leg, because *long leg X long leg* will only produce long legged birds. Each bird carries the short leg and long leg genes together and, as noted, if the two shorts come together, the result is death. In effect therefore the **norm** will be one quarter lethal, the same for long leggedness, and half will contain both long and short leg genes.

When breeding put the best short-legged birds together, and never those with longer legs. As a method
of improving fertility the feathers may be clipped, thus
allowing the birds to mate more easily. A further recommendation is to use young cocks (second year) with
mature hens. The usual procedure is to breed from the
same family thus ensuring that the main requirements
are 'fixed', improving the strain, but not introducing
foreign blood which could upset the delicate balance of
the colour or other requirement.

Figure 3.32 Japanese Bantams

JAVA BANTAMS

In shape, these are rather like Rhode Island Reds (with Leghorn-type tail), but in various colours – Mottled, Black and White. They have single combs. The Mottled variety looks rather like a heavy weight Ancona.

The USA standard weight is 28 oz. to 36 oz. the cock being the heavier weight. They were admitted to the ASP in 1960. At present they are not in evidence in the UK.

JERSEY GIANTS

The idea of a bantam in Jersey *Giants* seems a contradiction, but they do exist in two colours, Blacks and Whites. The large were produced in the USA from multi-crosses involving Javas, Dark Brahmas, Black Langshan and Indian Game. The Blacks in large were standardized in 1922, and the bantams, as noted, came much later.

The J–G is a massive bird with cocks exceeding 13lb. and bantam cocks are around 38 oz (in excess of a kilo), which is really big enough for a small table bird. Even so it will be noted that the size is less than an Indian Game cock at 48oz. maximum.

The breed is worth cultivating for its symmetry and attractiveness. The well rounded body, fairly high yet full tail, and stately carriage make for a handsome bird. Although yellow skinned the legs are very dark and without feathers, and this applies even to the White variety.

Kraienkoppes

Jersey Giants

Figure 3.33 Krainkoppes & Jersey Giants
Rare breeds in bantams

KRAINENKOPPE

Type: A gamey looking breed, rather like a smaller version of the Sumatra Game.

Origin: On both sides of the Duitch/German border.

Size: 26oz to 30 oz. the cock being heavier. (740 to 850g.).

Hard or Soft Feathered: Soft, but tends to be tight feathered.

Comb: Strawberry, referred to as 'narrow walnut'. Wattles short.

Tail: Full with quite strong, curved sickles and hangers; carried at an angle of 30 to 40 degrees.

Legs & Feet: Medium to long, bent at the hock; feet strong with four toes. Yellow in colour.

Beak & Eyes: Beak strong, yellow with whitish tip. Eyes red or yellow/red.

Description: A powerful looking breed, active and proud. Long body, curved breast and powerful legs.

Colours: Silver and Golden; these colours are similar to the Greys of other breeds and the Black Reds (with minor variations).

Characteristics: Active and aggressive rather like Game fowl.

Show Qualities: Bantams quite popular and are very attractive.

Production Qualities: Fancy fowl with show potential.

Exhibition Faults: Weak looking, narrow, faulty comb, twisted toes, excessive feathers.

Special Notes: A relatively new breed in the UK and USA.

La Fleche

Lakenvelder

Figure 3.34 Some Rare Bantams

LA FLECHE

This is an extraordinary bird, with its long body, fairly long legs (bent at the hock) and V-shaped comb, with fairly long wattles and white ear lobe. The tail is well spread, with full sickles. The large fowl was a product of the table poultry market, but is not standardized as a bantam in the UK, but one variety of the bantam exists (Black) in the USA,, but is rare.

LAKENVELDER

Also spelt Lakenfelder, this German breed is very striking, the plumage consisting of a a white body and the remainder black (neck hackle, saddle hackle and tail). The feathers are close fitting and the tail is long and fairly upright (45 degrees angle). The body is rather like a Game fowl with a long tail. Bantams exist in the USA, (1960), but are not standardized in the UK. This is a very attractive breed worth cultivating. It is around 20/24oz. in weight.

LAMONA

This is fairly new breed created in the USA; it was standardized in 1933 as a large fowl and, as a bantam, in 1960. The White is the most popular, but other colours have been bred such as Black, Buff, Columbian and Dark Brown. In shape it looks like a Dorking fowl (single combed) with horizontal body. Cocks reach 30oz.

LANGSHAN

See under Croad Langshan.

LEGBAR

These are a Campine-type breed with barred plumage produced to indicate the sex by colour; cockerels paler. Bantams exist in USA.

White

Brown

Black

Figure 3.35 Leghorns
Not to scale

LEGHORN

Type: Mediterranean, racy type body, excellent layer in large fowl, fair to good in bantams.

Origin: Italy from the town of Leghorn.

Size: Medium; 32 to 36oz. (910 to 1020g.) In the USA 22 to 26 oz.; in both cases the male is heavier.

Hard or Soft Feathered: Soft, but tight around body.

Comb: Single; large, upright in male, single fold on one side for female, but not obstructing sight. Rose comb is also found, but not as plentiful. See diagram for combs. Wattle long and even. Ear lobes almond shape and enamel white.

Tail: Upright, well spread for male and closed tail (whip tail) for female carried at 45 degree angle. In bantams, due no doubt to the reducing process from large, tails rarely seem to be as high or as curved as the large fowl.

Legs & Feet: Yellow or orange of fair length with a bend at the hock and four toes.

Beak & Eyes: Horn or yellow in colour, stout beak; eyes red, full.

Description: The model of a laying fowl, active and sprightly, fairly tall, with full tail.

Colours: White, Black and Brown (in bantams) , but other colours possible: Pile, Duckwings, Buff, Blue, Cuckoos, etc. In fact, in the USA there are 23 varieties which include such exotic descriptions as Black–tailed Red and even a Millefleur, which is interesting but appears unnecessary for a utility fowl.

Characteristics: A well balanced bird with a beautiful outline and carriage, but can be a little wild unless kept tame by frequent contact and handling.

Show Qualities: Many fine bantams appear at shows, but only in limited colours. The White is a purely self colour (free from yellow tinges), Black (Blue/black preferred) and the Brown is really a Black-Red with the male orange-red in hackle and shoulders and the breast black, whereas the female is a Partridge-type colour (see Old English Game).

Production Qualities: Average production for large is around 180 eggs per annum (some achieve much higher production), but the bantam varies and around 100 eggs is probably the norm.

Exhibition Faults: <u>Comb</u> short in cock and erect in hen; lobes red, squirrel or short tail; faulty colouring; dark eyes and legs.

Special Notes: Because Leghorns are a utility breed the bantam should be along the same lines. This has been difficult to achieve and therefore the breed as a bantam has never been very popular. In the USA the tail is broader at the base.

For exhibition birds special breeding problems arise in Blacks and Browns. Whites can be bred fairly easily to standard type. *Double-mating* (one pen for pullets and another for cockerels) is necessary for Blacks because the natural leg colour is black or grey; thus:

(a) Because legs are yellow there are difficulties with dark under-colour so mating must allow for the fact that under-colour in males tends to be weak and stronger in females.

(b) Cocks with white in sickles tend to produce better pullets because there is a tendency for these birds to have strong yellow pigment.

(c) Pullets have stronger black, but the shanks do not come as yellow as the male; they tend to be a dark colour. Accordingly, the cock with white in the sickles (less dense black plumage) will tend to produce better yellow in the legs of the pullets because the overall density will be reduced.

<u>Browns</u> have problems with a ruddiness across the wings which come from a very bright cock. In the male the desire for a pale yellow hackle, yet with a black breast and tail does cause conflict. Males and females must be selected very carefully to eliminate these problems.

<u>Combs</u> can cause difficulties – the fold for the hen and the straight, strong comb for the male. Breeding pens should allow matings which emphasize the separate requirements; eg, hen with erect comb to breed cockerels and weak comb on cock for pullet breeding.

Figure 3.36 American-type Leghorn
Courtesy: Irvin Holmes

MALAY

Type: Hard feathered, Asian-type heavy weight bird of great height, with broad shoulders.

Origin: Asian. Bantams bred down from large.

Size: Bantam males reach 48 oz (1360g.) so are quite large. In the USA they are 32 (pullet) to 44oz (cock).

Hard or Soft Feathered: Hard, very scantily clothed with bare patches on breast and on wing joints; brilliant feathers.

Comb: Half Walnut or half strawberry (opinions differ on the correct description). Head broad and overhanging eyebrows (beetle brows). Wattles very small.

Tail: Whip tail which slopes downwards, below horizontal.

Legs & Feet: Long legs with bend at hock. Feet strong and long with four toes. Colour a rich yellow.

Beak & Eyes: Strong, curved, thick with a fierce expression. Neck bare at front. Eyes light in colour: pearl, daw or yellow (any hint of red is quite wrong).

Description: A tall bird with sloping back, broad deep breast, long strong legs, and a ferocious expression.

Colours: Many and varied from Black Red (with Clay, Partridge or Cinnamon or Wheaton hens), Duckwing, Spangled, White, Mottled, Pile, Black and others. The colours are similar to Old English Game.

Characteristics: A pugnacious breed which is very strong. Sometimes referred to as the "Gangster of the Bantam World", but this is unfair because kept in a separate pen they give no problems except they outgrow their strength and sometimes have leg problems.

Show Qualities: Excellent birds for those who want

Ideal as drawn by Ludlow and bred by W F Entwisle

Modern Pair of Malays showing faulty tail

Figure 3.34 Malays
These have not changed since early days

something different in a rare breed. At present exact colours do not matter because there are so few bred.

Production Qualities: Show birds only, although the culled birds are big enough to eat. A hen will lay a clutch of eggs (about 10 to 12) and then sit and rear her chicks; started early she may rear three broods, but keep her in a separate shed and rear the chicks separately. They mature very quickly, but high protein food is advised to avoid growth problems, especially weak legs.

Exhibition Faults: Roach back, high tail, willow legs, wrong colour eyes, lacking beetle brow, faulty legs, single comb, too feathery, not tall enough.

Special Notes: The Malay comes from a very ancient race and possesses many characteristics not found in the Red Jungle Fowl and for that reason may have originated from a different ancestor*. Bantams were bred by Entwisle (ibid) from around 1890, selecting suitable large fowl and then also using Aseel. The difficulty in bantamizing is to retain the character with the traditional three curves of neck, back and tail.

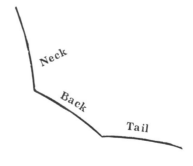

Figure 3.38 Essential three Curves of the Malay
See Keeping Jungle Fowl, J Batty

MARANS

Type: A medium size fowl, cuckoo or barred, with white skin and legs; dual purpose, utility breed renowned for very dark brown eggs.

Origin: France from the town of Marans.

Size: 24 to 32oz. (680 to 790g.)

Hard or Soft Feathered: Soft, but reasonably tight, fitting fairly close to the body.

Comb: Medium size and single with five to seven serrations.

Tail: Standard states 'high', but in practice is of a medium height.

Legs & Feet: Medium size, with white legs and feet, no feathers on legs. Four toes.

Beak & Eyes: Beak white or horn colour; eyes large and bold, bright orange or red.

Description: A fairly upright bird with a relatively long back, medium tail, full but not too high or spread, broad breast without obvious keel.

Colours: *Cuckoo* markings in three separate colours, being a variation of a blue\black with a lighter ground colour. **Dark, Golden** and **Silver.**

Characteristics: A utility-type fowl with a capacity for "roughing it" and producing very brown eggs as well as a good body size in the large.

Show Qualities: Getting the equal width bars can be difficult.

Production Qualities: Lay dark brown eggs so are in line with the large fowl.

Exhibition Faults: Feathering on legs, non-utility type, face and wattle other than red, wrong colours.

Special Notes: Faults which occur include patchiness
in the colour and the bars tend to be uneven on some
birds. The breed is very similar to the Barred Plymouth
Rock in barring.
Cuckoo means a light and a dark band in a distinct
and even pattern. Thus the following apply:

Dark Cuckoo: white/greyish with bands of blue/black.

Golden Cuckoo: bands of bluish grey with a golden
shading. Hackle bluish grey with bars of black and gold.

Silver Cuckoo: white neck and bars which are much
lighter than the Dark Cuckoo. This is therefore a di-
luted form.

The Barred Plymouth Rocks have achieved very high
standards in barring, but this has meant some loss of
the utility aspects. Marans breeders cannot afford to
meddle to the extent of losing the dark brown egg factor so the need for precise barring may be regarded as
unneccessary. Because of this fact Marans are not regarded by some as being as pleasing as other barred
breeds, even though the barring has improved considerably. In other words, they must be looked upon as a
utility fowl rather than a fancy one.
Marans in bantams produce very creditable results in
dark brown eggs and this must be maintained for it is
the distinctive feature of the breed.

Female

MARSH DAISY

This is a breed which took the poultry fancy by storm in the 1930s. It is a rather 'Gamey' looking bird, quite handsome, with tight feathers, rose comb, white ear lobes and legs a willow green. With an assortment of colours and its utility aspects there is much to offer. Bred especially for keeping in damp conditions (hence the name); it also had reasonable table properties.

Colours are Blacks, Buffs, Browns, Whites and Wheatens, the latter being popular.

In recent times, although a rare breed, it is in existence and being improved.. Whether bantams will emerge is not clear, but would be a worthy cause. A cross with, say, an OEG bantam, such as a Polecat or Clay coloured hen with a small Marsh Daisy would produce the desired result in a few generations.This would link in the colour, including the legs.

Figure 3.40 Marsh Daisies

MINORCA

Type: Mediterranean and therefore the laying type.
Origin: Spain.
Size: 30 to 34 oz (850 to 960g.); USA is around 2oz. lighter.
Hard or Soft Feathered: Soft, but tightly fitting.
Comb: Single with male upright and female with bend on one side. Rose combs appear in large fowl (UK), but not in bantams, except in USA.
Tail: Large upright tail well spread, with strong sickles. Carried at an angle of 35 degrees.
Legs & Feet: Black or slate for Black or Blue varieties. White for remaining varieties; four toes, medium length, thighs showing.
Beak & Eyes: Longish, stout and curved; beak to match plumage. **Eyes:** Dark brown in Blacks and Blues, and red in Whites and Buffs.
Description: Stately and graceful bird following Mediterranean type, horizontal carriage, large comb (female drooping), almond-shaped ear lobes, very active.
Colours: Blacks, Buffs, Whites, and Blue. The first three exist in the USA in single and rose comb.
Characteristics: Although racy, they are well adapted to domestication, and have a well made body formation as well as being good layers.
Show Qualities: Top class bird for shows; exhibit well and compete for top awards frequently. However, best in first year – tend to deteriorate in head points.
Production Qualities: Excellent layer for a bantam.
Exhibition Faults: Squirrel tail, foul feathering, wrong leg colour for variety, side sprigs to comb, white

in face, faulty lobes.

Special Notes: This very handsome bantam is worthy of support. Although they tend to be 'first year' birds, they can win in later years if maintained in good feather. Matters which should receive attention are:

1. Ear lobes and comb.

Must be enamel white and, in practice, as large as is feasible. Obviously this should not be carried too far with ear lobes like the Spanish fowl. There must be no wrinkles or marks, or discoloration.

The comb in the male should be upright with five even serrations (six points), and the female comb should fold over beak and then droop down one side without blocking vision.

Comb, face and comb are very important features for this breed. In total the points awarded are 40 in total. Experience indicates that only birds near perfect in these features will win top prizes.

2. Colour

The variety must be true to the variety specified. **Blacks** sholud be black with a beetle green sheen; **Whites** are that colour all over, including the fluff, with pinkish white on legs and beak; **Blues** should be a medium shade with darker top colour in the cock, and legs and beak as for Blacks; **Buffs** are a good, even colour, neither reddish nor yellow and legs and beak should be pinkish white.

Note: Generally double mating is not essential, but when combs have to be improved, or lobes to be bred larger, careful selection of the birds for the breeding pen is advisable.

Female bent comb

Figure 3.41 Minorcas

Handsome birds which win prizes.

Pullet Breeding for Head Points: Cockerel: thin comb tending to droop is mated to sound hen with good head points.

Cockerel Breeding: Hen with straightish, strong comb mated to cockerel with strong upright comb with six points and blade following neck, but not too near.

Figure 3.39 Pile Modern Game Cock

MODERN GAME

Type: A tall-standing, elegant breed, originally by crossing breeds which were Game in character, but also included a whip tail.

Origin: British

Size: In large is classified as 'Heavy' (Cocks up to 4.10k), but in bantams is 16 to 22oz. (450 to 620g.) which is the same size as Old English Game, a light breed.

Hard or Soft Feathered: Hard; tight feathering.

Comb: Single, fine. In males is dubbed close to the skull so that the effect is to give a snakey appearance.

Tail: Whipped and fine, carried just above horizontal, not to be spread or feathers to be broad.

Legs & Feet: Long legs clearly visible, with four toes and no hint of duckfootedness. This can be difficult because some fine specimens may stand on their toes.

Beak & Eyes: Medium; eyes prominent; colours to match plumage (usually red or dark).

Description: A hard feathered, small bodied bantam, with long legs, whip tail, tremendous reach, and trained to utilize all its points.

Colours: In the USA there are 18 varieties, and in Britain the colours are Black Reds (Partridge hens); Black Red Wheaten, Brown Reds, Golden Duckwing; Silver Duckwing, Birchen (really Greys), Piles, Buffs, Blue Red, Silver Blue, Lemon Blue and in Self colours: Buffs, Blacks, Whites and Blues.

Characteristics: Purely a show bird which has been improved over many years by careful selection; very friendly, fairly hardy, reasonable layers some strains.

Birchen

Black Reds

Figure 3.43 Modern Game Male & Female

Must have 'lift' and 'reach'; elegant, compact body without
deep keel; tail to be almost horizontal.

Show Qualities: Win many top awards because they require great dedication to breed and train. A top specimen is quite breath taking – usually a male.

Production Qualities: Fetch high prices if top show strain.

Exhibition Faults: Not complying with exact colour specifications in standards, including wrong colour eye or legs, flat shins, duckfooted, roach back, cocks without spurs, short in body, wrong carriage, thickset head, any feature which departs from grace and elegance.

Special Notes: The body should be broad across the shoulders narrowing to a very small area at the back for the tail; shortness of back is essential. There must be no hint of coarseness or the bones will be heavy and not in keeping with the racey appearance and elegance required. Keels should not be too deep and the body should be nicely curved.

Colours: Although the OEG bantam colours can be a guide it should be appreciated that whilst it is often said that in Game there is no such thing as a bad colour (the shape being all–important), this is not the case for Moderns. Special points to watch are:

Black Red Partridge: <u>Male:</u> Hackle will be a very light red, with the shoulders and back crimson, wing bow and bay chestnut/red, with remainder a faultless rich black. <u>Female:</u> Light partridge colour, evenly marked and without ruddiness across the wings; hackle gold striped with black, salmon on breast, tail black.

Birchen: This is really a black and silver grey combination, known as Dark Greys in OEG, but the description 'Birchen' continues to be used, which really implies a brown colour, which it is not.

Brown Reds: The hackle on the male and his top colours are really a yellow/lemon colour and not the reddy /yellow colour of Brown Reds with OEG. The female is beetle green with a yellow/lemon hackle lightly striped-with black.

Legs and eye colour: Confusion exists on the appropriate colours which are :

Black legs; Dark eyes	Birchen, Brown Reds (gypsy faced in both breeds)
Yellow legs; red eyes	Pile
Willow Legs; red eyes Silver	Black reds, Duckwings, Gold and

Breeders used to suggest that the show birds did not make good stock to breed from so a separate pen was kept for breeding only. This appears to overlook the fact that the show winners could also produce further winners. My daughter bred Modern bantams in a number of colours and we found no difficulty in breeding from show specimens provided they were strong and fit. In Piles, basically Red and White in colour, when the colour begins to lose its strength a cross with a Black Red should prove remedial. Then breed back to a Pile cock or hens with the stronger colour base.

Some advocate double mating to produce pullets and cockerels separately. In this it is possible to produce extreme examples from each pen of each sex.

4

THE BREEDS II

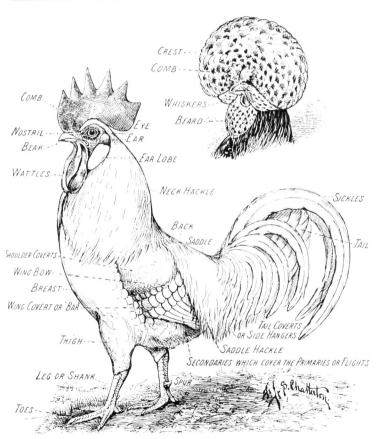

Figure 4.1 Points of the Bantam
A guide to terms used in the book.

NAKED NECKS
See *Transylvanian Naked Neck*.

NANKIN BANTAMS

Type: A natural and true bantam, gingery buff in colour on the body, with a black tail. It is a very ancient breed.

Origin: The origin is said to be Asia, but whether this is stictly correct is difficult to establish. Since it is a natural bantam Japan or China appear to be likely sources.

Size: 24 to 30oz. (680 to 850g.) the cocks being larger.

Hard or Soft Feathered: Soft; fairly plentiful in feather, but not excessive.

Comb: Single or Rose, but tend to be single, although rose may reappear occasionally.

Tail: Fairly large with curved sickles. Cock: sickles black and remaining feathers copper or chestnut. The shape resembles the Rosecomb.

Legs & Feet: Clean legged with four toes; fairly short. Colour slate blue or white with a bluish tinge.

Beak & Eyes: Colour white; originally the standard (Entwisle) stated short and small, but the modern standard now stipulates longish and fine.

Description: A well rounded bird with wings fairly low; prominent breast and a fairly upright stance; large sweeping tail gives symmetry.

Colours: One colour, ochre and cinnamon. Takes its name from the yellowy colour.

Characteristics:. Active, with a proud carriage and beautiful feathering.

Show Qualities: Likely to become a favourite at shows, but this is still uncertain after being rescued from obscurity by dedicated fanciers. Entwisle writing in the 1890s lamented its scarceness. Later writers such as W H Silk, founder of the British Bantam Association, writing in 1951, stated: *Once the most widespread of all bantams and progenitors of nearly all buff varieties. Still standardized on the Continent, but unlikely to be revived here.* How fashions change!

Production Qualities: Purely a show bird.

Exhibition Faults: Faulty comb, females without black ends to tail and males with all black tails, small tail, wrong colour legs, wrong coloured plumage, lacking jaunty character, and white ear lobes.

Special Notes: Genitically this is an important breed. The Sebrights were bred from Nankins crossed with others and it is believed that they were widely used for developing other breeds where buff was required. There are no special breeding problems.

Figure 4.2 Nankin Bantams

New Hampshire Reds

Norfolk Grey cock & hen

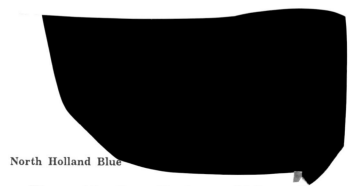

North Holland Blue

Figure 4.3   Some Bantams which are Scarce
Not to scale

NEW HAMPSHIRE REDS

In shape this breed originally resembled the Rhode Island Red, but with selection is now shorter in the back, more rounded, and slightly smaller. It lays brown eggs.

There is one variety with the male reddish bay or chestnut with a black tail. The female is similar with the lower neck feathers having black tips.

This is an attractive American breed with both large and bantams, although the bantams are not in the UK at present. Size is around 34oz. for a cock and 30oz. for a hen. (ASP).

NORFOLK GREY

A British breed introduced in the 1920s, and re-semble a Grey Old English Game. Leghorns were the other side of the mating so although the carriage is Gamey the long wattles on many specimens indicate the Mediterranean influence. The large fowl breed has undergone a revival and it would be pleasant to see bantams, which would obviously be a utility type.

The colour for both sexes is a black body and the male has silver grey hackles and shoulders; the neck hackle of the female is also silvery.

With a dark Grey OEG bantam cock and a Leg-horn hen there should be no difficulty in producing the Norfolk Grey bantam. It must have dark legs and ear lobes without any white which would take a few years to establish without blemish.

NORTH HOLLAND BLUE

This breed is along the lines of Barred Plymouth Rocks being fully barred in blue-grey. The white legs are lightly feathered on one side.

This is a tall bird which develops quickly. In colour the cock is a lighter shade than the hen, but both must be fully barred.

The comb is single with medium size wattles. The cock has a U-shape between tail and neck hackle, but the female has a longer back.

The bantam version is in the USA, but not listed in the British standards. Size around 34oz. cock.

OLD DUTCH BANTAMS

See *Dutch Bantams*

Figure 4.4 American Style OEG

Black-Red   Cock - very stylish
Figure 4.5 Varieties in OEG.

OLD ENGLISH GAME

Type: Agile, aggressive with other birds, but with distinctive characteristics; rather like miniature Red Jungle Fowl modified by selected breeding.

Origin: England, but kept in Scotland and Wales for a very long period. Some doubt that they are miniatures of large Old English Game, but there is no proof either way, except they do resemble the large Game in many respects.

Size. Small, cobby; female 18 to 22oz. (510 to 620g.) and males 22 to 26oz. (620 to 740g.).

Hard or Soft Feathered: Hard feathered, feathers fitting close to the body.

Comb: Single and in males usually trimmed (dubbed); there are Modified versions which include birds with Muffs and Tassels.

Tail: In English-type birds very small tail with little or no main sickle feathers. In the USA and Australia they prefer the older type which have large, fully sickled tails, like large OEG.

Legs & Feet: Rounded legs, finely scaled, colour to match plumage; four toes with back toe firmly on the ground and **no hint of being duckfooted**. Legs usually white, except in darks such as Greys and Brown Reds.

Beak & Eyes: Generally white or horn to match legs.
Eyes: Red, or dark for dark coloured birds.

Description: A small bodied bantam, active in carriage, legs which bend at the hock, tight feathered, wings which are close to the body and tip is under tail, broad at the shoulders, flat backed, and narrow at the rear, with a small, compact tail. (except USA style).

Colours: There are numerous colours and although it is often stated that in Game there is no such thing as a "Bad Colour", in reality, when a definite colour is specified , the bird in question should comply with the description in the standard.

The more popular colours are:

1. Black Red with Partridge hens. This means cock with scarlet hackles and shoulders and tail and breast black. The hen is a soft brown colour with black and lighter markings which resemble a Partridge and the wings are free from rust colour.

2. Black Red with Wheaten hens. Cock as 1. but a lighter, more orangy shade for the scarlet. The Wheaten is a light creamy colour the colour of wheat.

3. Spangle. The male a deep burgundy colour with black breast and tail and small speckles in white, evenly distributed over the body. The female is similarly marked and is of a deep partridge colour with a small black line near each spangle.

4. Duckwings. These present an anomaly because the description comes from the presence of a mallard–type wing bar of metallic blue found on the wild duck. There are two main types:

(a) Golden Duckwing and, (b) Silver Duckwing.
Black breasted and yellow replacing red in Black Reds for Golden Duckwing and silver white for Silver Duckwing. Females rather like partridge hens, except the body colour is a darkish grey mixture for Golden Duckwing and light grey for Silver.

5. Self Colours: Black, Blues, Whites should all be pure in colour without foul feathering.

Pile Cock

Figure 4.6 Further Colours OEG. (not to scale)

6. Pile: Males are white instead of black in Black Reds, but with bright red on hackles and shoulders; the hens are white with a yellow hackle, spotted or shaded breast (creamy) and depending on the intensity of the red the overall colour is white or white with red or yellow markings. They are given names like Custard Piles or Blood-wing Piles based on the depth of colour. Legs should be white, but many are seen with deep yellow legs which may be a sign of an Indian Game cross.

7. Furnesses and Polecats: A mixture of black, brown, red and yellow. In the Furness cock the shoulders are a red colour and a variation, Brassy-backed, the shoulders are yellow. Usually the hackle is black. The Polecat is a similar mixture. In all cases the hens are basically black with intermingling of another colour. Although the purity of colour is doubtful these are attractive birds.

8. Brown Reds and Greys: Basically black birds, although may have signs of dark partridge in the female feathers. Brown red cocks have a black breast (sometimes laced) with hackles and shoulders an orangy yellow and females have a yellow stripe in the hackle.

Greys are similar but substitute a silver grey for the orange yellow. Both are scarce in bantams. Legs and eyes should be dark.

9. Blue Variations: Once blue is introduced into any variety it has a tendency to stay. The result is that many sub-varieties have been produced, such as Blue Tailed Wheatens, Blue Reds, Blue Duckwings, Lemon Blues and many others.

10. Crele and Cuckoo: These are barred varieties, sometimes blue/black, like other barred breeds, and others red and or yellow, making a very beatifully marked bird.

11. Rare Colours and Off-Colours: Many other variations exist ranging from Ginger Reds and Black Breasted Dark Reds which are seen in large Game to off-colours that have been produced by a chance mating, when the main aim has been to produce better *share* Those are also Black and White Splashes, Brown Breasted Reds, and many mixtures that defy accurate description. They have to be shown in *Any Other Variety* classes.

Characteristics: Lively breed which are quite hardy and present no problems in keeping, or hatching eggs. and raising chicks. Friendly to owners and very interesting to keep because of colours and show requirements.

Show Qualities: Often win *Best in Show.* Are fairly easy to prepare, but there is tremendous competition so only highly bred stock will get top places.

Production Qualities: Purely show birds although are quite reasonable layers.

Exhibition Faults: Shape is vital so any bird which does not have a cone-shaped body, with a very short flat back, and hard feathering, will not win. General faults are duck-footed; loose feathering; light coloured eyes; wrong colour legs; weak narrow face; white ear lobes; deep keel; flat sides; crooked breast bone; long, straight legs; narrowness; twisted or weak hackle and any weakness in constitution.

The heart shape viewed from the top is critical and must be present or any bird without the desired qualities must fail. It must be flat with **strong shoulders** and very short; in fact, in good specimens there is very

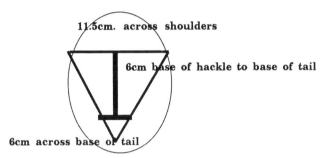

11.5cm. across shoulders

6cm base of hackle to base of tail

6cm across base of tail

little gap between the bottom of the hackle and the base of the tail. The diagram above shows the measurements of a 7 month old cockerel; the shoulders were 115 mm across, base of tail 60mm and back 60mm. The bird in question, a Black Red Partridge was selected at random from a batch of chicks hatched late summer. A female sister had similar measurements except her shoulders were 100mm and back depth was 70mm. These birds are not given to show the ideal, but the principes involved. A shorter back should be the aim, but remember the birds must remain active and productive.

A cock tends to be more upright than the hen and the hackle slightly longer, so this would account for some difference. The cock's hackle should not be too profuse and hang well over the shoulders, which would shorten the back, but would be quite wrong on a hard feathered bird.

Special Notes: OEG bantams up to show standard are obvious from a mere look in the show pen. The shortness of back, no thickness at the back and between the legs, a slight upward curve under the tail, and legs at the correct angle. Birds must be handled when judged. Sometimes critics suggest that birds with poor colouring win at shows and yet have been bred simply by crossing for shape. This is simply not true because getting the overall shape and correct carriage is a feat in itself. However, it is conceded that more attention should be paid to colour perfection and birds should be penalized if faulty when in a specific colour class.

At recent shows some major faults seen were:

1. Wrong colours in Partridge hens (rust on shoulders); Blacks which were too tall and Blues which were also too tall, had dark blue lacing and were very similar in build to Minorcas.
2. Cocks which stood on tiptoe and the back toe was raised from the ground. This and duckfootedness must never be allowed in a winning bird.
3. Wings trailing, due to split wing or due to lack of tightness in feathering.
4. Tails of males which were practically non-existent. The problem with the short tail style is that sickles can be pulled out, making the cock look narrower at the back. This is faking and must be watched so any cock with no sign of any sickles, even if very weak, should be penalized, otherwise the OEG bantam will become a rumpless fowl.

Never show Old English Game when unfit or mopy. Make sure the cocks are dubbed and try to leave a few weeks for the comb to heal. Good dubbing is an art so make sure it is done by an experienced person.

OLD ENGLISH PHEASANT FOWL

This is an old breed of British origin, being rather similar in shape to the Hamburgh.

The body is full fronted and prominent, legs medium, bending at the hock, and the full tail carried high; the comb is Rose, quite detailed, with a short leader which points downwards. Ear lobes are white and almond shaped.

The main **colours** are **Gold** and **Silver,** along the lines of Hamburgh Spangles, but the Gold is mahogany in colour on shoulders; heavy spangles in black.

Bantams are not standardized which is surprising and should not be difficult to produce. Hamburghs and similar breeds, such as Rosecombs, could be used as a foundation. Size would be around 32oz. (910g).

(Male)

Figure 4.7   Old English Pheasant Fowl
Worthy breed for developing into bantams.

ORLOFF (Russian Orloff)

This is a bird which is shrouded in some mystery. It is believed to originate in Russia being imported from Persia by Count Orloff-Techesmansky. The breed may be related to the Malay and this is indicated by illustrations of the breed, although these do vary, some birds being more upright than others.

Support for the breed being quite separate stems from the unusual head which sports a beard and muffs. The flattish comb has been described as a half raspberry shape, which is covered in small 'mounds' and channels.

The body is broad and long and the neck is long; the legs are strong and yellow in colour.

As befits a large breed which scales around 8lb. the bantam should be in the region of 36oz, this being the maximum.

Colours are varied, but White, Spangle, Black and Mahogany have been bred in large. The same colours should be feasible in bantams. In the USA there is a Black Tailed Red bantam as well.

At present bantams are not recognized, but they have been in existence from around 1924 when they were owned by a Mr Prentice; these were Mahogany in colour, which is a mixture of red and deep-reddy brown, with grey and black markings in the hackle. The Spangled are quite beautiful, rather like Black Red Partridge in Old English Game (see illustration).

Like all rare breeds there is fascination to bring them back so they are bred once more. This seems especially so with Orloffs, with their link with Russia and the unusual shape, and comb combined with muffs.

<u>Black</u>

Round, Ball-like

Wings of
modern birds
tend to touch
ground

Indentation between
leg feathers & body
now virtually disappeared

<u>Outline of Breed</u>
Compare USA style given under Cochins

Figure 4.12 Pekins of Different Colours.

During the mid 1900s the breed became much shorter in the
leg and moved towards being more like Japanese, although
still quite distinctive. Thigh and shank feathers now merge
with the upper feathers and (hopefully) this process seems to
have reached its maximum.

Characteristics: A very domesticated breed which will thrive in all conditions, although the heavily feathered legs mean that in inclement weather they must be kept indoors.

Show Qualities: First class, but need a great deal deal of attention to ensure perfect colouring and feathering.

Production Qualities: Purely ornamental. For breeding usual to trim the fluff around the vent of both male and female. The foot and leg feathers are also trimmed.

Exhibition Faults: Too tall, wrong shape, faulty comb, wrong colour, broken or dirty feathers on legs or feet, eyes wrong colour, legs other than yellow, slipped wing, any other defect.

Special Notes: For a detailed description of the many colours see the *Standards*. In brief terms these are:

Black: Beetle-green black throughout.

Blue: Pigeon blue with darker hackles.

Buff: Even buff colour throughout.

Cuckoo: Dark slate barring on a lighter colour.

Mottled: Black with white mottles evenly marked.

Barred: Definite barring of black/white, the colours being quite distinct.

Columbian: As for Light Sussex.

Lavender: A silver-tinted lavender (not a light blue).

Partridge: Male Black Red and female a light partridge colour (see OEG of same colour).

White: An ultra-white overall.

Watch for **scaly legs** and if there is any sign of roughness on the scales, rub with sulphur ointment, which usually stops it before it becomes embedded.

Malines (Cuckoo)

Modern

Langshan

Old English Pheasant Fowl ▼

Marsh Daisy

Charles Francis

Orloff (Spangled)

Orpington (Blue)

Marans
(Dark Cuckoo)

Naked Necks
(Transylvanian)

New Hampshire Red

North Holland Blue   Charles Francis

La Fleche

Malay
(Black Red)

POLAND (Polish: alternative name or Plural for Poland)

Type: Ornamental type with a full crest, longish body and quite active. Very old breed; bantams developed around 1885.

Origin: Difficult to establish; may be Poland, but many believe the name comes from "Poll", referring to the crest or the raised portion of the skull. It appears that the breed is not found in Poland.

Size: 18 to 28 oz. for pullets and cocks respectively. (510 to 790g.).

Hard or Soft Feathered: Soft, reasonably close to the body.

Comb: Very small or none at all; when present a Horn type. Wattles small, but on bearded or muffled not seen.

Tail: Large size, high and carried at angle of 45⁰ for male and 40 for female, above horizontal. All feathers long and full; male sickles well curved.

Legs & Feet: Clean legged; four toes; colour slaty blue; fairly long.

Beak & Eyes: Beak: dark blue (Bearded) or horn; Eyes: reddish bay.

Description: A full, rounded body, flat back, wings large and tucked in; full tail and unusual head which contains a crest only **or** is also bearded with no wattles.

Colours: Non-Bearded: White Crested Black, White Crested Blue; White Crested Cuckoo.

Bearded: Chamois (White Crested Buff); Silver, Golden, White, Blue and Black.

Characteristics: Like other light breeds is a non-sitter; is a very active bird. In fact, the non-bearded

Blue White-Crested
Figure 4.13 White Crested Polands
No beard, but wattles and ear lobes.
Found in Blacks, Blues and Cuckoo.

Figure 4.14   Bearded Polands (Polish)
Chamois, Silver (laced), Gold (laced), and self-colours White,
Black and Blue.

have a white factor, which affects the soles of the feet and the skin; whereas the bearded have a blue factor which tinges skin, beak, and soles of feet.

Show Qualities: Primarily a show bird and with the correct markings and beard, where appropriate. It can achieve top level prizes.

Production Qualities: Fancy fowl only, although a reasonable layer.

Exhibition Faults: The crest is of vital importance so any faults on head would be serious (see under special notes); wrong type of comb; legs not slaty blue; no colour band in front of white crest of Black, Blue or Cuckoo Crested; very short hackle.

Special Notes:

Crest: The head has a protuberance on which the crest grows. In the **male** this must be circular and full, with no splits or parting, or falling to one side and it falls evenly from a central point. In the **hen** the crest should be globular. The nostrils are very large and wide.

Colours:

White Crested with Wattles: Crest white with colour band at front same colour as body. Body colours: **Blacks** – Green black with plenty of sheen; **Blues** – slate blue, self colour or laced; **Cuckoo** – even barring slate or light grey. The 'Blue' was regarded as being slate, self blue or laced (Andalusian–type), but there appears to be a movement towards a self colour (UK).

Bearded Polands (Colours which follow may appear in non–bearded – *USA standards*):

    (a) Laced and

    (b) Self Colours: Black, Blue and White.

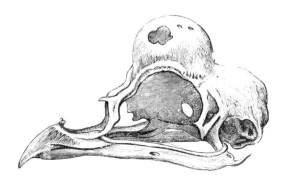

Figure 4.15 The Skull of the Poland
Shows the protuberance and cavernous nostrils

Chamois: Rich golden buff in main colour with lacing on each feather in white or light cream; crest same colour; beard* buff laced with white; tail laced; Hen is buff with lacing all over.

Silver (laced): Silver-white colour with black lacing; crest black at roots; hackles and primaries tipped with black; tail laced with black. Female silver white with lacing on each feather of lustrous black.

Gold (laced): As for *Silver,* but replace silver white with rich red bay.

Note: Young stock may not achieve the perfect markings first year and older stock may get the odd white feather in the laced crest and these variations should be recognized. However, any sign of crest being pulled or tampered with is faking and should be disqualified.

---

* USA standards specify beard, but British prefers 'Muffling'; which includes whiskers; the terms are therefore interchangeable unless used where there are no side whiskers.

Special Management:

1. Use water founts which avoid getting crests damaged – open dishes or bowls are unsuitable. Food dishes should be of the type that allows the birds to feed without damaging the crest or beard.

2. Take care to see the crest is encouraged to grow and in inclement weather keep birds under cover.

3. Cut crest and beard when breeding or use sellotape to raise above eyes, thus avoiding problems.

4. Spray or dust the crest and vent area regularly to kill mite (avoid getting in the eyes).

Not An Easy Breed: These very beautiful birds are worthy of the attention of all dedicated bantam fanciers, but they can be difficult to breed to a high standard; without first class crests they are below expected standards.

Double Mating: This is unnecessary, but some fanciers seem to believe that the laced varieties might be improved by selective breeding in two pens – one for males and the other for females. It is a practice best avoided, but if great improvements can be made the experiment may be worth while.

PLYMOUTH ROCKS

Note: There is confusion on the name because the varieties are known by different names without the pre-fix of 'Plymouth' - Barred Rocks, Rocks, Buff Rocks, etc.

Type: In large, a heavy breed which lays large tinted eggs; regarded as a utility type bird. Some have been bred down from the large, whereas others may have very little large blood in them.

Origin: Large from USA , but bantams in UK may have come from the Scots Greys for the Barred and some of the self colours from the Wyandottes.

Size: 22 to 30 oz. (620 to 850g.), males being the heavier.

Hard or Soft Feathered: Soft, but moulded around the body showing the shape, but not tight like Game.

Comb: Medium size, single and upright, with even serrations. Wattles medium and ear lobes small and the natural red colour of the face and comb.

Tail: Low with sickles of medium length. No apparent cushion.

Legs & Feet: Clean legged with four toes. Thighs well covered with feathers.

Beak & Eyes: Beak yellow; eyes red or bay.

Description: A fairly upright, with longish neck, full, deep, broad breast, short broad back, with wings fairly high and close to the body.

Colours: Barred, Buff and Partridge. Blacks and Whites also seen.

Characteristics:. Tend to be slow in feathering; tall, well made, quite hardy.

Show Qualities: Difficult to achieve excellent barring.

Buff Rocks

Barred Rocks

Figure 4.16 Plymouth Rocks

Production Qualities: Some strains good layers.
Exhibition Faults: Foul feathering (depends on colour); barring too wide or indistinct; stub on legs; wrong under colour; split wings; faulty comb; high tail; cut away fronts; knock knees, duckfooted, thin thighs; in Buffs uneven colouring.
Special Notes: The Buffs are now produced in a deep even colour. Careful selection of birds is essential and never include 'washed out' colour in breeding stock.
Barred are also excellent, but it seems that the best exhibits are the result of double mating. The aim is to get clearly defined black bands on a white ground colour. Males are narrower in barring. The sort of formula needed:

Pullet Breeding
Hens perfect Barring X Male with light, clear bars.

Cockerel Breeding
Large Hens with dark barring X Males with perfect barring

Not all agree with this approach, but it appears to be the favourite. Any Blacks produced should not be bred from.

Partridge: Male is a combination of red and black. Tail, breast and visible underparts green-black; neck hackle and base of tail black with red lacing; wing bows red.
Female: Deep red bay with triple lacing on main feathers; main tail black., but coverts and webs red, laced with black.
These are produced from one pen without double mating which can be difficult.

REDCAP

The Redcap is an old breed which is related to the Old English Pheasant Fowl and the Hamburghs. It was always regarded as a very commendable layer, but the emphasis on the enormous comb appears to have rather spoilt the utility aspect. Because of its affinity to the county of Derbyshire it is often give that prefix, but many years ago it seems to have been very popular in Yorkshire.

The body in traditional, tending to be 'Gamey, with a well developed tail and fairly upright carriage In colour it follows the Black Red pattern with black half-moon spangles. The gigantic comb is the main feature which on the large fowl reaches 4in across and 5in to the tip of the spike for the cock and about 2in. wide for the hen. This is on a breed which is between 5 and 6lb.; ie, a medium sized fowl. Bantams around 26oz (740g.).

Figure 4.17   Redcap
A breed with potential as a bantam

RHEINLANDER

This is a German breed of long standing being known as early as 1884. In shape there is resemblance to Old English Game, but with a rose comb which makes it resemble the Hamburgh. In addition, since there is no call for a short back the body tends to be longer than in Game.

Colours are varied and include Partridge, Black, White, Blue, Barred and Cuckoo.

Tails are large and magnificent following the Hamburghs, but more cobby in body shape. Ear lobes are small and white.

Figure 4.18 Rheinlander

RHODE ISLAND RED

Type: Utility type fowl; heavy breed, lays brown eggs.
Origin: USA and named after the state in which they were developed from the original parentage of Red Malays and Leghorn and Asiatic breeds. They originated around 1903 and in the USA the bantams were recognized in 1940 (single comb) and 1952 (rose comb). In Britain were around in the 1920s, but too large.
Size: 24 to 32oz. (680 to 910g), the heavier weight is tho cock
Hard or Soft Feathered: Soft, although not abundantly feathered like the Brahma.
Comb: Single, but Rose comb permitted and appears occasionally. Fairly large and upright with five points or serrations. Rose comb not seen in bantams in UK. Medium wattles.
Tail: This must be of medium size only and carried at 20 degrees for males and only 10 degrees for female. In other words, it is almost level with the back, being just above horizontal. It should be well spread or deep, not whipped like a Malay nor high with long sickles like the Leghorn.
Legs & Feet: The thighs should be large and visible and shanks and legs should be of moderate length. Viewed from the front, the legs should be well apart. The colour is deep yellow with red down the side.
Beak & Eyes: Beak of moderate length, curved and reddish horn. Eyes: red or reddish bay.
Description: A long bodied fowl, brick shaped (rectangular), with prominent breast, but gently curved, almost straight at the front, and carried horizontally; wings large and strong, well tucked in.

RIR cock with tail too high; hen with weak keel.

Ideal brick-shaped RIRs

Figure 4.19 Rhode Island Reds

Colours: A rich deep chocolate colour with a rich red under colour. A White variety is also recognized in the USA.

Characteristics: A very hardy breed; suitable for keeping inside or out; good layer; become quite docile.

Show Qualities: Provided the deep chocolate red colour can be obtained, with the brick shaped body (essential to have long keel) and deep yellow legs, this breed can win top awards.

Production Qualities: Very favourable in a utility breed.

Exhibition Faults: Wrong colour (too light); lack of keel; lack of lustre on plumage; long tail or carried at wrong angle; faulty comb; fish eyes; white on ear lobe; colour other than red and black where permitted by standard; sign of 'frizzle' feathers; light under colour; absence of utility qualities.

Special Notes: Originally an ordinary red colour was the criterion, but over generations the colour has become deep chocolate red.

Tail: Green-black in male (red near saddle) and female (two top feathers may be edged in black);

Wings: *primaries* – lower webs black ; *secondaries* – *upper* coverts black; *flight coverts* black; remainder red.

Hackle and Neck: *Male:* Deep glossy red. Female: Red with black ticking at base.

The Rhode Island Red is the Black-tailed Red type of bantam. Although double mating is not advocated it should be recognized that where colour is getting weak, a good breeding male should be very strong in black markings on wings, tail and even on the back, but not on breast or wing bows. The sound female must have

deep colour in the wings.
This sel;ection of a strong colour in the vital areas
means that as much black as possible is being trans-
ferred, thus getting the deep chocolate colour required.
Rhode Island Whites should follow the pattern of the
RIR, but be a conventional white colour overall.

Sickles too
long & pointed

Figure 4.20 Rosecombs: ideal by Ludlow.
These days more rounded end of sickle feathers essential

ROSECOMB

Type: A true bantam bred from early times, possibly for hundreds of years, and possessing remarkable features in body, wings, ear lobes and comb.

Origin: British.

Size: Small; 16 to 22oz. (450 to 620g.) the cocks being heaviest.

Hard or Soft Feathered: Soft, but is really near enough to be hard feathered, the plumage being tightly fitting around the body.

Comb: Rose with detailed "work" and no large spikes or hollows or ridges. Immaculate with broad main part and tapering to the leader, rising slightly and beyond back of head. (see diagram shown for Hamburghs).

Ear lobes must be large, enamel white and round; fine like kid without any blemishes or discoloration.

Tail: Male: Full with curved, broad sickles almost forming a circle; however, should not go too low to complete the circle (45 degree angle). Female: long and upright, neatly folded into a half fan (35⁰ angle)

Legs & Feet: Thighs almost covered at the side by the low wings; shanks short and fine and with no sign of feathers. Feet should have four toes. Colour black for Black variety; slate in Blues and white in Whites.

Beak & Eyes: Short with slight curve and black, horn or white for Blacks, Blues and Whites respectively.

Eyes: Brown (Blacks) and reddish bay.

Description: A cobby bantam, very small, with very full breast, short back on male, full tail and very decorative comb and face, the whole to be symmetrical.

Colours: Black, Blue and White. The Black is the most popular; must have brilliant green sheen.

Rosecomb where tail has shortened with age.

Figure 4.21 Rosecombs

Characteristics: An ornamental bantam bred for perfection and purely for showing.

Show Qualities: Excellent show bantam, but requires great attention to achieve the standard requirements. Lobes are difficult to perfect and may blister or lose some of the whiteness or the perfect round shape. Tails can be too long; sickles should be broad at the end, but some specimens with very long tails have narrow ends which is wrong. After the first season tails may get too short.

Production Qualities: Purely show birds.

Exhibition Faults: Wrong type of feathers; faulty comb; face other than brilliant red; marked or misshapen ear lobes; incorrect plumage colours; tail with narrow feathers, or too long or short; narrow frame; faking of any kind on comb, face or tail.

Special Notes: Colours are as indicated: Blacks must be Green-black without any purple sheen or barring; Blues are an even, medium blue without lacing; Whites should be pure white. In the USA there are 26 colours!

Double mating is usually practised in Blacks only, but the theory applies to all three if breeding for better combs. If for colour then the Double mating usually applies to Blacks only.

Breeding for Combs:

Male Breeding Pen: Sound male X Females with long leader and comb, thick and round ear lobes, and short backs.

Female Breeding Pen: Very sound hen X Cockerel with comb short at the front and very large, thick ear lobes.

Not all would agree with this approach, but since combs and ear lobes are so important any approach which improves the quality is worth trying.

Breeding For Colour:

Male Breeding Pen: Male with brilliant colours **X** Female with broad fronted comb and long leader, with curved long tail, and plumage colour dead black with little lustre.

Female Breeding Pen: Male short in back with large lobes and exceptionally brilliant sheen **X** Female with very good, brilliant green-black plumage.

Note: Males with red in hackle tend to produce brilliant plumage on the females.

At one time Blacks and Whites were bred together; this was done to improve the white lobes, but it also caused problems with colours.

Another old trait was trying to produce very small birds - dwarf bantams - but Entwisle felt this was wrong and would lead to problems.

Once the first season is over, there may be difficulty in maintaining quality. If ear lobes, tails and other features are to be maintained as long as possible, the fancier must give top class accommodation with shade in sunny weather and dry shelter in winter. Also good quality small-size layers' pellets should be fed regularly, thus giving adequate protein to maintain body requirements.

RUMPLESS BANTAMS
(Standardized as Rumpless Game Bantams)

Type: Although 'Rumpless' may be found in soft feather breeds as well as hard, the latter is more usual. In the standardized type they are rather like slightly over-sized Old English Game, but with no tail.

Origin: Uncertain, but known in Persia and various other countries, such as Japan and South America, hundreds of years ago. Aldrovandus described them in 1615, in the days of Oliver Cromwell. At one time it is said that they were common on the Isle of Man; another report stated Belgium and in another the West Indies.

Size: Small being 18oz for pullets and 26 for cocks (510 and 740g.).

Hard or Soft Feathered: Hard, although Rumpless are also found in Soft feathered birds. Araucanas can also be Rumpless (see entry).

Comb: Small to medium and upright, like Game bantams, but Rumpless are not dubbed.

Tail: None.

Legs & Feet: As for OEG; clean legged with back toe pointing backwards, and no hint of duckfootedness.

Beak & Eyes: Slightly curved and colour to match legs. Eyes: Red or dark, depending on colour of plumage.

Description: A short backed Gamey looking bird with legs bent at hock.

Colours: As for OEG bantams, but not so strict.

Characteristics: In Rumpless Game a sprightly breed following the lines of OEG, but deformed physically so it is unable to grow a tail.

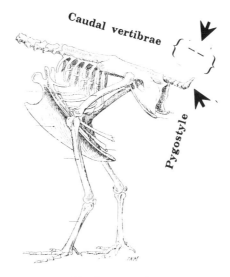

Figure 4.22 Skeleton of Bantam
Shows part missing in rumpless condition

Figure 4.23 Rumpless

Show Qualities: Not seen very frequently.
Production Qualities: Egg production variable dependent on strain.
Exhibition Faults: Any sign of tail; faults under OEG.
Special Notes: Rumplessness occurs when birds have part of the structure of the body missing; ie, the caudal vertibrae and pygostyle.   The birds lack the 'Parson's Nose'. In some case the rumplessness is only partial.

Research

Much research has been conducted on the condition. Charles Darwin, Tegrtmoier, and others stated that some strains may produce normal birds as well as rumpless.

Further and later research showed that the results from mixed breeding were variable. In one case *Normal Male X Rumpless* hens produced 17 Rumpless and no Normal. On the other hand, in another case, equal numbers of Rumpless and Normal were produced. However, the later breeding results had the effect of modifying the genes affecting rumplessness.

On the evidence available it is usually suggested that the characteristic is dominant, but it seems that this can be modified by continuing to breed with mixed stock.

The Rumpless Araucana exists as a separate breed and was first standardized in ASP (1976) well after the first Rumpless fowl was reported and there is a suspicion that these may not be the true Araucanas, but there is no evidence to support this theory except normal Araucanas were in the UK before that date.*

Note: When the condition occurs in stock which is not Rumpless then these should be regarded as abnormal specimens for the breed and should be culled. Thus a well known fancier bred a Rumpless Orpington which was obviously a freak in a breed that always has a tail.

---

*An interesting article by Richard J Billson sums up the history in *Poultry Club Year Book*, 1994.

SCOTS DUMPY

A dwarf-like fowl, which appears in large fowl as well as bantams, although the smaller version are not seen very often. They have long, low bodies and extremely low legs and come into the category of Creepers, and therefore are related to the Japanese bantams and German Creepers, described earlier. Accordingly, when bred **Short leg X Short leg,** they carry a lethal gene. **Colours** are Cuckoo, Dark and Silver Grey.

Bantams have been bred, but they are quite rare. Other than the fact that they are unusual and interesting Dumpies have little to offer when compared with many of the jaunty natural bantams available or the utility types which are both beautiful and useful. The weight should be in the region of 22oz. (620g.).

Figure 4.24 Scots Dumpies

SCOTS GREY

Type: The Scottish National breed, which is quite ancient and the large fowl has been a barn-yard fowl for hundreds of years. From the type – shape and carriage – it would appear that OEG were used in their make-up. It is a utility type which lays large white eggs.

Origin: Scotland; bred from large.

Size: 18 to 24 oz. (510 to 680g.)

Hard or Soft Feathered: Soft, but is really a hard foothured type, but this description is limited to Game.

Comb: Single and upright, medium size.

Tail: Carried high with long sickle feathers. Barred like rest of plumage.

Legs & Feet: Similar to OEG. The British Standard suggests that the thighs should be wide apart, "but not as prominent as Old English Game". This is quite out of character because wide apart thighs is a serious fault in Old English Game.

Beak & Eyes: Beak whitish and curved; eyes are said to be "amber".

Description: Typical Jungle Fowl type of body – long and compact with prominent breast; strong legs with bend at hock.

Colour: Cuckoo. The basic ground colour is blue white and light grey. The bands should be black and straight across on body, thighs and wings, whereas they tend to be angled on other parts. Sometimes it is suggested that Barred Plymouth Rock and Scots Greys are the same in barring. This is not strictly true. In Plymouth Rocks the very bold black barring is straight and even, but the Scots Grey is more crescent-shaped (curving)

Figure 4.25 Scots Greys
Cuckoo markings (cf. Barred Rocks)

and the colours are lighter; the spaces are a light blue and the bars are more indefinite.

For these reasons the suggestion often made is that the correct description is "Cuckoo" rather than barred.

Characteristics:. An agile bird which is beautiful as well as useful.

Show Qualities: Very showable and can win top awards.

Production Qualities: Good layer of largish eggs.

Exhibition Faults: Lack of barring; foul feathering with brown, red or other colour, not of an even shade, white in tail; short in legs; stork legged; faulty comb.

Special Notes: This is an interesting breed which has always had some dedicated followers, but not in large numbers. Obviously there is more support in Scotland and, it seems, always a few dedicated fanciers who keep them going.

Figure 4.26 Sebright Turn of Century
Note type has not changed.

SEBRIGHT

Type: An ornamental type bantam which was developed from other breeds about 200 years ago. It has hen-feathering, delicate lacing and a rose comb.

Origin: The originator was an Englishman, Sir John Saunders Sebright, Baronet, Member of Parliament for Hertford and a keen animal breeder and falconer. He crossed the Nankin with Polands, a Hamburgh (and /or Rosecomb), and a Henny Game cock.

Size: Very small; 18 to 22 oz. (510 to 22g.), the cock being larger. USA standard (ABA) slightly heavier.

Hard or Soft Feathered: Soft, but feathers close fitting around the body.

Comb: Rose which is square at the front and tapers to a point at the back (the leader), turning slightly upwards. The comb is full of small serrations and should be even all over, without bumps or hollows. The face, comb, ear lobes and wattles should be red in the cock and mulberry or gypsy in the hen. In the original breed both sexes had very dark faces and, if possible, this feature should be the aim.

Tail: Hen feathered, which means male and female have similar tails so the cock has no sickle feathers. The tail should be spread out rather like one side of a fan and the feathers should be laced around the edges; poor specimens have no lacing or have spangles at the end of the feathers, or suffer from frosting or mismarking. Carried high, in the region of 70⁰ angle above horizontal (ABA Standards).

Legs & Feet: Legs are fairly short with thighs wide apart. In colour they should be slate blue; four toes.

Figure 4.27   Sebright Cock with Excellent Lacing
Lacing carries a quarter of the points. Note the short back
and hen feathering.

Beak & Eyes: The beak should be dark horn, but, in the Golds, dark blue is allowed. Eyes quite full with dark ring round (cere), and a dark colour – brown or black.

Description: A jaunty breed with an upright carriage, wings pointed downwards at an angle, broad prominent breast, short back, short hackle, and tail with no sickles on male.

Colours: Gold and **Silver.** Other colours have been bred and in the USA some extraordinary varieties have been attempted, but nowadays the original colours remain – Gold and Silver. In fact, there seems little point in developing other colours.

Characteristics: An ornamental bantam much admired; jaunty and colourful, with many unusual features.

Show Qualities: Excellent, but difficult to breed birds with all the requirements to a high standard.

Production Qualities: Purely show birds; some difficult to breed because of infertility problems.

Exhibition Faults: Faulty lacing; uneven colour in Gold and creamy colour in Silvers; single comb or badly shaped comb; feathers not rounded or almond shaped; curved sickles on male; tail at a distinctly wrong angle; long back on male (some tolerance is allowed in female); white or wrinkled ear lobes; shaftiness in feathers; lack of character – not strutting and trembling when excited (especially male); long legs; any other trait or feature not in accordance with the standard.

Some faulty birds are illustrated, indicating the birds which may be bred.

Silver: Lacing Poor; mismarked.

Gold: Comb lumpy and Drooping Tail

Figure 4.28   Sebrights with Faults.

Special Notes: This fascinating bantam is not recommended for beginners because there are many problems in getting the correct lacing and other features. With some strains there are serious fertility difficulties and it has been suggested that the answer is to use cocks with sickle feathers, thus enhancing the fertility. The author has bred hen cocks in Old English Game for many, many years with no problems, provided the weather is warm. In other words, breed from May onwards for best results. Exercise and a properly balanced food is essential, with the correct level of protein; small pellets, formulated for laying hens, appear to be the answer. There should be a plentiful supply of greens and scratching litter in the form of leaves, grass clippings and other offerings from the garden, which ensure that the birds are kept active and fit. Many experienced fancier finds that he gets reasonable results.

Double Mating: The practice of having one pen for females and another for males is not essential, although some breeders do use special matings to get specific results. Since the aim is to get perfect lacing it is usual to mate on the basis of getting delicate, yet bold lacing. If trying to improve males it is usual to use a heavily marked male and a normal female. For female breeding the male should be well laced and standard type, with a female that is very heavily laced in all parts. Opinions differ on the exact approach, but many fanciers suggest that Silver and Gold should not be bred together, because this spoils the colours; in fact, at one time pure Silvers were almost lost because of mixed breeding. The **Gold X Silver** does provide sex linkage.

SHAMO

This is a Japanese breed and the bantams are a smaller version of the large fowl, which is essentially a fighting bird. Originally the breed may have come from China. The shape of the body is similar to the Malay, with a sloping back and tail set low, but in bantams is rather like the Aseel, with medium length legs.

The feathers are very scanty and fit closely around the body; the breast is quite full and wings well tucked up. Feathered legged versions have been seen, but we have no experience of these. Legs are not as long as Malays (more medium length), but they are quite strong and thighs should be quite visible.

The comb is the walnut or a modified rose. It should be quite small; wattles are very minimal.

Colours: Similar to Malays: Dark Red, Brown Red, Buff Columbian, Brown, Spangled, Wheaten, Black, and Red and White.

Typical Shamo Bantams

Figure 4.29 Shamo Bantams

SICILIAN BUTTERCUP AND SICILIAN FLOWERBIRD

These are a product of Sicily and therefore may be regarded as unusual Mediterranean breeds. The body shape does resemble an Andalusian, but with a larger and higher standing tail.

THE COMB

The outstanding feature is the comb which is cup shaped with the upright points standing at each side rather like horns. The *standard* for the **Sicilian Flowerbird,** in existence around the 1920s stated:

> Comb cup; a single leader beginning at base of beak and joined to a cup shaped crown set firmly in the centre of skull and surmounted with well-defined and regular points; of medium size and fine texture, as free as possible from internal growth; an opening at the back is permissible.

The major difference between the two breeds is the size. The large Buttercups are in the region of 6lb. and the Flowerbird about two thirds the size. Bantams would therefore be in the region of 28oz (790g.) for the larger and 16oz. for the Flowerbird. These are approximate because they are well built birds and it may be difficult to get very small weights.

Colours: Buttercups: Brown (Black–Reddish type); Golden; Silver; Golden Duckwing and White. The Gold is mainly red-bay in the male and golden-buff, spangled with black in the female. Silver follows the Gold pattern, but silver–white ground colour. The Duckwing is similar to the Old English Game Duckwing.

Colours: Flowerbirds: Mahogany and Spangled.

The **Mahogany** is a Black Red type with a **dark** mahogany red colour in male and **dark** brown in female.
The **Spangled** are similar, but with the addition of spangles which are 'scattered' across the feathers.
The main problem in the breeds to get the perfect comb without any spikes inside the cup.
At present bantams are not recognized, but the unusual comb merits the creation of ornamental bantams.

Mahogany Flowerbird

Silver Buttercup

Figure 4. 30 Sicilian Buttercup & Flowerbird.

SILKIES

Type: Ornamental-type breed in the sense of having a furry like covering instead of the normal feathers. This webless plumage is referred to as "Silk" - hence the name.

Origin: Some Eastern country, possibly India, China or Japan. They were seen in China by Marco Polo at the end of the thirteenth century.

Size: Quite small and only in recent times recognized as a bantam in Britain; before that regarded as a standard large fowl of 3 to 4lb. USA weights 32 to 36oz. which is not much different from the standard British size, which at one time was 2 to 3lb. but is now one pound heavier. British bantams are expected to be 18 to 22oz (500 to 600g.), the male being heavier.

Hard or Soft Feathered: Soft with the lack of webbing which makes the plumage very soft and fluffy. Any hard feathers are a serious defect.

Comb: Described in different ways, but is cushion shaped which is at the front of the crest; the latter trails back on the male (3.75cm), and is like a rounded powder puff on the female. There are **bearded** and **non-bearded** varieties. Ear lobes should be turquoise or mulberry; comb and face are mulberry.

Tail: A cushion or mound, made up of soft feathers with no sign of shafts of feathers.

Legs & Feet: Legs are short and have light feathering down the outside of the leg and on the outside of the middle toe. Colour of legs lead-blue; nails blue-white. It must have five toes.

Beak & Eyes: Slate-blue and eyes black.

Description: A round-bodied bird with hair-like

<u>Black, White & Partridge</u>

Often described as
Rose or Walnut,
but, because of its
shape, the more
correct term is 'Cushion'

<u>Comb of cock</u>

Figure 4.31   Examples of Silkies.

feathers, mulberry face, feathered legs, crest and unusual cushion comb.

Colours: White, Black, Blue, Partridge and Gold.

Characteristics: A tendency to go broody after laying
a clutch of eggs; eg, 15, and, once chicks are feathering,
to lay the requisite number of eggs and then go broody
again. Very docile and adaptable creatures.

Show Qualities: Does well at shows.

Production Qualities: As a broody is second to none,
but the smaller bantams are not able to cover many
eggs. Not generally acceptable for eating because the
skin and flesh are dark and even the bones are black.

Exhibition Faults: Hard feathering of any type (usually in
tail); scaley legs; vulture hocks (see Sultan for example); light
eyes; only four toes; wrong colours in specific colour class;
lack of crest or faulty; red face; green on beak; soles of feet
with green tinge; any indication of a cross with a normally
plumaged bird.

Special Notes: This unusual breed has been kept for hatching
and rearing chicks for generations. To give additional size
and to reduce the silk (chicks can get tangled at the front and
hang) some fanciers cross with Wyandotte or some other
heavy breed.

Colours which are self should be the colour stated without
any other mixture. Whites are pure white and Blacks are
greeny-black; Blues are an even colour without lacing; Golds
are a deep buff.

Partridge are rather like badly defined Black-Reds with the
cock being golden-red with black breast, and the hen a
golden-brown with detailed mixtures of black and brown resembling a Partridge (see Black Reds under OEG).

Medical problems

Two major problems may exist: *scaly legs* which should be
avoided by the regular use of sulphur ointment, and Marek's
Disease (paralysis) in some strains. Fortunately, Marek's Disease can be avoided by vaccinating when chicks.

SPANISH

The Spanish breed is similar to the Minorca with the addition of a very large area of white on the face; sometime this is referred to as a "Clown's Face", such is its size and outlandish appearance. Nevertheless, it has its followers and the long face-piece which stretches below the wattles is a credit to the clever selection and breeding by the fancier. However, there is a recommendation (ABA) that this combined white area of face and our lobes should not be extended to the level where it is regarded as grotesque.

The cock has a skull which is both deep and broad and is surmounted by a single-type comb which is straight (the hen's turns on one side); the ear lobes and face are deep and broad and extend well below the wattles which are connected by a "bib" at the front. This is the most important feature of the breed. Half the points are awarded to all aspects of the head and its features. The white face should be like white kid gloves, without blemish or mark or discoloration (eg, pink, purple or darkish marks). Neither should there be excessive coarseness, with the white parts being uneven, sometimes cauliflower-like, or puffed up and almost closing the eyes.

The main colour is Black, but at one time there was a White, and in the USA there is a Blue. The Black should be a beetle green free from purple bars. Legs should be black or dark and eyes are brown. Tail is carried at 45° for cock and 40 for hen and is large.

Bantams are in the USA, (standardized in 1960 in Black) and can be bred by crossing a bantam of similar type with a Spanish male; in the USA it was found that an OEG hen was suitable, followed by selection*. The main problem is to get the white face; this appears to be a dominant feature, but may be restricted by other genes and therefore the problem is to find the breed which harmonizes. Size should be around 30 to 34oz. (850 to 960g).

Figure 4.32 White Faced Spanish Fowl
This pair are showing very long faces; in fact, the cock's is on the long side.

* Reported by Fred P Jeffrey, *Bantam Breeding & Genetics*.

SULTAN

The Sultan is a rare breed, but one that appears to interest fanciers so that it never seems to disappear. They appeared in Britain in 1854 via Constantinople, being imported by a Miss Watts.

There is agreement that they are related to the Polands. The main differences are: smaller size, five toes, vulture hocks, and a different body shape (back much shorter).

The body is fairly long and deep, but due to the position of the tail the back appears quite short. The legs, with five toes, tend to be short and pale blue in colour; they are covered in feathers and the thighs have downward spiky feathers, known as vulture hocks.

The face is fully muffled with beard and whiskers and the head is surmounted by a crest; the nostrils are large. The comb is the horn type (V-shaped) and quite small, following the pattern of the Houdan.

The description refers to the White variety which is the one usually seen. In the USA there are also Black and Blue varieties, but they are scarce.

In breeding show winners it is essential to get the head and leg features correct, the other aspects not being so difficult. Chicks are quite hardy so there should be no problem breeding them. In inclement weather they should be kept under cover.

In Britain the bantams are very rarely seen, but should not be difficult to produce. The large fowl only weigh about 5lb for cocks so selection, and crossing with a Poland bantam should bring down the size, which should be around 18 to 20oz. (510 to 570g.).

Plymouth Rock (Barred)

Polands (Gold)

Redcaps

Rhode Island Red

Scots Greys

Sussex (Speckled)

Charles Francis

Faverolles (Salmon)

Hamburgh (Gold Pencilled)

Houdan

Indian Game (Dark)

Leghorn (Cuckoo)

Nankin Bantams

Crest large
Comb
diminutive

Feathered Legs
Vulture Hocks
Five toes

Figure 4.33 Sultans

Dark Face

Very long
tail

Figure 4.34 Sumatra Game

SUMATRA GAME

These are beautiful birds, with long graceful bodies and
the cock has a long flowing tail, There seems little
doubt that the breed is related to the Japanese long-
tailed fowl, even though it does originate from Sumatra.

The principal colour is Black, but many years ago a
friend who was quite big in the breed, did produce
Whites. In the USA they have also bred Blue bantams.
Tho colour is the deepest of black with a brilliant green
sheen, an amazing sight, and, to complement this col
our, the **face** and **Pea comb** are a dark, dusky colour
known as Gypsy faced. **Eyes** are large and bright and
preferably a dark red or other dark colour.

The **legs** have four toes and no feathering, and these
should be of moderate length, bent at the hock and the
back toe firmly on the ground. The cock may have two
spurs on each leg (known as rose spurred) and this feature is acceptable as normal. Along with the beak, the
legs should be dark olive or black.

The long flowing **tail** starts at the saddle hackle and
then, with a profusion of broad feathers, long and flowing, it declines so it is below horizontal. The whole
should be symmetrical so the bird when standing looks
quite statuesque.

Although a Game bird it must not be shown in other
than a class for its breed or for *Any Variety Game* ; it
is no relation to Old English Game or other types of
Game. Although the tail is so vital to type, strangely, it
does not get extra points, not being listed separately.
Type and **Head** get 20 points each. **Size** 20 to 24oz.
(570 to 680g.).

SUSSEX

Type: A utility type-bird, being one of the main birds (the Orpington the other) which supplied the markets of London with high class table fowl. A whole industry grew up around the breed in a wide area above Eastbourne in Sussex, stretching upward to Tunbridge Wells, the Heathfield area being the centre. The bantams are miniatures of the large breed.

Origin: British, but crosses were used to produce specific varieties. It must be appreciated that there are many poosible varieties, although not all have existed in bantams.

Size: 28oz for hen and 40oz for cock (790 to 1130g.). In the USA the weights are about 4oz. smaller.

Hard or Soft Feathered: Soft, but of medium length.

Comb: Single with five well defined points.

Tail: Medium in size carried at an angle of 45⁰ degrees above horizontal for cocks and 35 for hens.

Legs & Feet: Legs stout and well apart, colour white.

Beak & Eyes: Prominent and large and reddish bay.

Description: A large body with prominent breast and long flat back, with white skin and legs as befits a top table bird.

Colours: Light, Brown, Buff, Red, Silver, Speckled and White. In the USA they list the Birchen which appears to be the equivalent of Silvers.

Characteristics: An active fowl although not as quick as the lighter breeds; the laying qualties are good for a general purpose fowl.

Show Qualities: Does well, especially the Light Sussex, which looks excellent with bright red face and the colour combination.

Figure 4.35 Points of the Light Sussex.

Faults:
1. Too tall; cut-away breast; whip tail.
2. Hen; as 1 above.
3. Too stocky; long neck; very short back; large comb.
4. Coarse; feathery cushion; feathery thighs.

Production Qualities: Favourable layers in some strains, but it must still follow the pattern of a table fowl.

Exhibition Faults: Not having the squarish, yet long, flat backed body; wrong colours; legs and skin not white; any character opposed to type; too fluffy in plumage; rose comb; feathered legs; five toes; hackle too feathery; any other feature which is not a character of the breed.

Special Notes: Bantams have existed since the 1920s. It was said that Speckled were the first variety, But this cannot be certain because a report in 1930 stated that Light Sussex had been around 12 years before that year, whereas Speckled came in 1927. In fact, the *Poultry Year Book* for 1927 stated:

Light Sussex bantams are being bred, but are still in an imperfect state.

There was no mention of any other variety and, since it would be reporting on 1926 (the previous year) this seems conclusive that the Lights were the first variety.

COLOURS:

Light Sussex: Columbian-type plumage, which is the most popular variety. The overall colour is white with the hackles striped greenish-black; the tail is also black, with the lesser coverts laced. The neck hackle black stripes now tend to be very broad and black, yet it must be appreciated that there should be a white margin on each feather. Eyes orange.

Brown: A rich mahogany colour with the black striped hackle and black tail. The female is a browny Partridge colour with a pale breast of wheaten brown. It is really a Black-Red type. Eyes red.

Light Sussex

Silver Sussex

Figure 4.36   Sussex Varieties

Buff: In markings like the Light Sussex, but the white is replaced with a good, deep, even buff. **Eyes** red.

Red: As for Lights, but a deep red as the main colour and, once again, striped hackles. The under-colour is slate. Because of the colour this variety is sometimes said to resemble Rhode Island Reds, plus the striped hackle; whilst this is true the shape should be different, the Sussex being deeper with a very broad back. **Eyes** orange.

Silver: These are similar to the Grey found in Old English Game being blackish, but with neck hackle, shoulders and tail hackle a silvery grey (male). The female is black with a silver striped hackle and a laced breast, the breast being a little lighter than the rest of the body. Some argue that the laced breast is out of place in a Sussex. **Eyes** are orange.

Speckled: There is a suspicion that Spangled Old English Game bantams, are in the original makeup. Speckled Sussex are of course a form of Spangle and follow the colour pattern for that variety. The ground colour is dark mahogany with a brilliant sheen on the male. The speckles should be spread in even fashion and there should be a small black bar separating the white speckle from the normal colour. With age there is a tendency for too many speckles to appear as well as too much white in the tail of the cock. **Eyes** red.

Whites: These are white all over. They appear to be out of place with the other varieties because they do not have the striped hackle. In fact, they are not very popular. **Eyes** orange.

THURINGER BEARDED

A German breed with a round beard and in a variety of
colours. In the USA there are Black, Blue, White,
Spangle (Gold and Silver). It is not available in the
UK.

TRANSYLVANIAN NAKED NECK

This breed originates from the Transylvanian area of
Hungary and Rumania. The main feature is the absence of feathers on the neck, making it appear rather
like a vullture, because the skin becomes red and tho
skin wrinkled. The characteristic comes from a dominant gene which means that it may be transferred to
other breeds.

The Transylvanian Naked Neck is long in the body with
a fairly long tail. In some respects it resembles the
Rhode Island Red but with a larger tail and the loss of
hackles. There is a tuft behind the single upright comb.
Due to genetic reasons feather tracts are missing and
this causes the lack of feathers.

In the USA there are six varieties of bantams: Black,
White, Blue, Buff, Cuckoo and Red.

Weights are 24 to 32oz. (680 to 910g.).

TUZO

This is a Japanese natural bantam which is along the
lines of the Aseel and Shamo. The body is tightly feathered, the breast full and rounded, with strong wings
tightly held, and the tail set at horizontal level.

The head is thickset with a strong beak, and the rose
comb should be very small; wattles minimal.

Legs should be strong with a bend at the hock and of
medium length. Weights quite variable from 28 to 44oz.
(790 to 1250g.).

Figure 4.37 Thuringer Bearded.

Figure 4.38 Transylvanian Naked Neck

Figure 4.39 Tuzo-type bantam
Strong head
Eyes very light

Figure 4.40 Vorwerk

VORWERK

A German breed which superficially looks like a thick-set Old English Game with a longer back, especially in the hen. The male is buff in body with a black hackle, head and tail. The female is a similar colour. The tail is fairly short and well below the level of the head. It is a utility type and must be judged as such. Bantams are 24 to 32oz in weight (610 to 910g.), the cocks being the heavier.

WELSUMMERS

Type: Medium sized, utility breed, developed for its very deep brown eggs. The history is well recorded and shows how the breed was selected on the basis of the eggs being purchased by market customers.

Origin: Welsum in Holland.

Size: 28 to 36oz. (790 to 1020g.)

Hard or Soft Feathered: Soft, but fairly close feathering.

Comb: Single and upright, extending beyond the head at the back. Wattles medium size.

Tail: Tail fairly high and wide, with the male having well developed sickle feathers.

Legs & Feet: Four toes; legs medium length; in cock thighs visible and in hen tending to be hidden by under feathers. Legs yellow.

Beak & Eyes: Beak strong and fairly short, horn or yellow; eyes red .

Description: A moderately upright carriage and well feathered. The cock resembles a conventional Black Red, somewhat "mismarked", because the breast has brown mottles. The hen is a rich Partridge colour, but with a breast which is deep red (instead of normal salmon), and her tail is black with brown pencilled outer feathers. This deepness of colour is no doubt the reason for the brown in the breast of the male, and the rich golden brown of his hackle.

Colours: One colour; in large a Duckwing also.

Characteristics: A rather handsome, medium sized breed which is docile and breeds well and produces very distinctive coloured eggs.

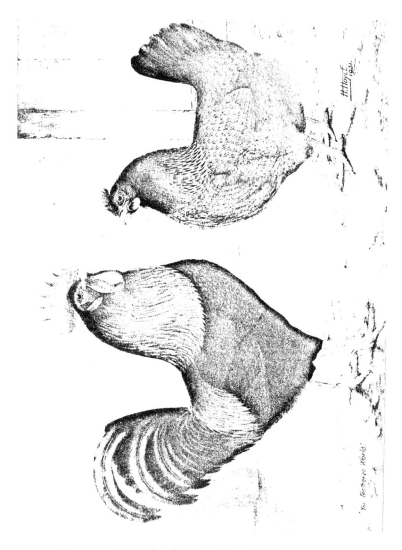

Figure 4.40 Ideal Type for Welsummers

Many bantams in the past lacked fulness of breast and looked
too much like OEG. The breed has changed since arriving in
this country.

Show Qualities: Must be utility type, but is attractive enough to win top awards. There is still some difficulty in getting the multitude of colours required for top birds. Theoretically this should not arise because the standard was framed to avoid double mating; unfortunately, fanciers insist on unnecessary features.

Production Qualities: Quite good, although never a top layer. Dark brown egg important.

Exhibition Faults: Feathers on legs, faulty comb, ear lobes other than red, not the correct combination of black and red on breast of cock, light breast in female, striping in male on hackle or saddle, any feature which indicates lack of utility features.

Special Notes: *The standard has been drawn up to avoid double mating so the fancier has to aim for the correct type and then for showing has to select those which come nearest to the standard. Initially the bantams did not lay brown eggs, but this problem has been overcome.*

Figure 4.41 Typical Welsummer bantam hen.
Lacks depth and fulness of breast.; not a utility type.

WYANDOTTE

Type: Miniature of the large Wyandotte; heavy breed; excellent layer. Bantams came about in different ways, depenent on variety, and therefore variable in laying abilities.

Origin: USA, where after an abortive start as the American Sebright, it was standardized as 'Wyandotte' (1883), based on the name of a Red Indian Tribe*. The first colour was the Silver Laced Wyandotte.

Size: 20 to 28oz. (570 to 790g.), the male being heavier.

Hard or Soft Feathered: Soft, but the rounded shape of the body discernible. Some of the modern birds tend to be too fluffy.

Comb: Rose, wide and even,; broad at front and with a leader which curves downwards to follow the line of the top of the head. Head broad with moderate wattles, overall colour red.

Tail: Follows the curve of the cushion, wide at the base and carried at a moderate height. Angle above horizontal 40 degrees male and 30 female.

Legs & Feet: Medium in length, bright yellow in colour, with four toes.

Beak & Eyes: Stout beak which is curved and yellow in colour, except Blacks which are black with a yellow tinge.

Description: Medium sized, very rounded with shortish legs, fairly tight feathering, a short broad head with tight, firm rose comb; active and productive.

* An alternative is after the name of a ship 'Wyandotte' owned by a Mr Houdlette, senior. See Laced Wyandotte Club report for 1994 (see p. 208).

Figure 4.42 Wyandottes

Buff Wyandotte

Cuckoo Wyandotte

Colours: Barred, Black, Blue, Blue Laced, Buff, Buff Laced, Columbian, Gold Laced, Partridge, Red, Silver Laced, Silver Pencilled, White. **In the USA there are 18 varieties:** Barred, Birchen, Black, Black breasted Red, Blue, Blue Red, Brown Red, Buff, Buff Columbian, Golden Laced, Lemon Blue, Partridge, Silver Laced, Silver Pencilled, Splash, White, and White Laced Red.

Past Colours: Buff Columbian, Black and White Spangled (Ancona type), Pile, Black-laced White, Copper (Golden Duckwing type), Cuckoo (similar to Cochin), and Mottled.

Characteristics:. Docile and friendly birds; do not fly and therefore low fencing possible; plump; good layers in some strains; excellent foragers when conditions correct – essential or they may get too fat.

Show Qualities: Excellent birds for exhibiting, keep in good condition. Must get the globular-shape of body.

Production Qualities: Satisfactory in many strains. Body quite plump.

Exhibition Faults: Stubs on legs; lack of size; very tall; body not rounded; beefy or faulty comb; long in back; narrow body; pale eye; faulty colours; tail too high; legs other than yellow; coarseness; poor lacing on laced varieties.

Special Notes: The many and varied colours make the breed very difficult to understand and whether such proliferation can be justified is doubtful. Whites are popular as are Blacks. Partridge, Pencilled, and Laced; they have active clubs.*

---

* See the *Poultry Club Year Book,* 1994 for reports from the separate clubs.

Ideal Types Female & Male

Figure 4.43 Points of the White Wyandotte.

COLOURS:

Laced:

Laced means there is an edging around the feather in a different colour. In Wyandottes it is single, but other breeds have double lacing; eg, Indian game.

Faults are: 1. Horse shoe lacing (partial only). 2. Full or part double lacing. 3. Mossy or streaky feathers. 4. V-shaped lacing (instead of rounded). 5. Irregular line of black.

Silver: Very handsome; Silvery white with black stripe in neck hackle; each feather laced in a regular fashion.

Gold: Golden brown ground colour; and as for Silver.

Blue: Red brown with blue lacing. In male hackles and saddle are darker.

Buff: Even, rich buff colour with white lacing. Hackles striped with white down centre. White under colour.

Figure 4.44 Silver Laced Wyandottes

* The USA standard (APA) treats many breeds under the heading of 'Partridge' as if identical, but Wyandottes are not the same as Plymouth Rocks in the British standards. The female Wyandotte should be the colour of a dead oak leaf; ie, Partridge as in OEG, but in APA the ground colour is deep reddish bay and the illustration shows this dark red colour not partridge. The British standard for Partridge Plymouth Rocks follows the USA standard (APA).

Pencilled Wyandottes

Pencilled in this connection means fine crescentic (curved) marks on each feather, in the form of lacing, often in triple form and varying in width and darkness of colour, depending on the type of feather.

Partridge*: Male is a Black red type with head of red and the rest of the hackle becoming lighter through orange to lemon at the base, with a black stripe on each feather. Top colours are red as in a Black Red. The breast, legs and tail should be green-black.

Female: Ground colour is Partridge, the colour of a dead oak leaf, with concentric rings of black on each feather.

Silver Pencilled: as for Partridge, but a silver-grey ground colour.

Figure 4.45 Partridge Wyandottes

The Silver Pencilled is as above, but a steel grey colour instead of the medium brown in the female and silver white in the cock instead of red and orange.

Barred/Cuckoos: These have bars which follow the pattern of Barred Plymouth Rocks illustrated earlier.
Black: Beetle green plumage with dark under-colour.
Blue: A medium blue without lacing.
Buff: Self colour of a solid, even buff colour right through to the skin.
Columbian: Follows the colour pattern of the Light Sussex and Light Brahmas. Essentially white with neck markings and tail in black.
Red: Overall red which is rather like the utility type of Rhode Island Red, exhibition types are now deep chocolate colour. Hackles are striped black and the tail is also black. The under colour is dark or slate.
White: All over white. Do not keep or breed from creamy birds or those with foul feathering. The **type** must be absolutely correct and perfect,, pure white.

Standard Points
Each variety has its own points scale and therefore fanciers are referred to the appropriate *Standards* for the detailed breakdown.

Double Mating
Separate pens are essential for breeding males and females up to show standard. These include:

Blacks:

Male Breeding Pen:
Male with bright yellow legs and black to skin.
x
Female with dusky legs and sound under colour

Female Breeding Pen:
Male: Bright yellow Legs with sound eye and
light under colour.
X
Female: Good standard type with yellow legs
and sound under colour.

Note: In this way it is possible to achieve the yellow
legs and sound black colour. Mated together without
selection female legs will be a dusky colour and male
under-colour will be unsound. Remember this should
be quite dark to comply with standard. See also description for Black Leghorns.

Partridge and Silver Pencilled
These must be double mated or the required standard
will not be achieved.   This segregation, once accom-
plished, must remain intact, not crossing one type with
the other. It has been said that Partridge Wyandottes
need such special selection in double mating that they
might be regarded as two separate varieties.

Male Breeding Pen:
Male with rich orange hackle and saddle, with
black centre stripe in feathers but not to full
extent. Back rich red *not* maroon. Black parts
(breast, legs, tail, wing bars etc.) raven black.
X
Female: large with good, sound brown colour
and black stripe down hackle (pencilling is
unimportant)

Female Breeding Pen:

Male: Standard type with very sound and plentiful lacing. Breasts are best marked with red.

X

Female: Good standard type with yellow legs and sound colouring (rich light brown) and each feather clearly pencilled with a dark shade all over, except the tail which should be black. The hackle should be striped with black.

Silver Pencilled are similar, but a good silvery grey colour is expected, with variations in hackle similar to Partridge, which was at one time called the Gold Pencilled, showing how closely related they are.

Note: As would be expected, with all birds with lacing and "pencilling" the markings must be as perfect as possible.

Laced Varieties: Double Mating

Cockerel Breeding

Std. cock heavily laced, strong in black, no white in tail or white fluff

X

Female (large) with sound black colour on silvery clear hackle with no sooty marks, but clear stripe.

Do not breed from female with necks which are brassy

or sooty because this will produce poor male colouring. Some moss or lacing on the breast of the female should not affect the soundness of the cockerels.

Female Breeding Pen

Male with sound under-colour with excellent breast lacing and lacing under saddle hackle

X

Hen with dark neck hackle and pure leg colour (avoid green or spotted legs)

NOTE: With all double mating it is as well to try different combinations because what is expected does not always work out.

Importance of Type:

With the emphasis on colour and markings the breeder sometimes finishes up with a type which looks too much like some other breed, such as the Orpington. This must be avoided by selecting birds which have the correct, rounded body and the cock should be broad breasted and deep bodied, with the short, U-shaped space on the back between the hackle and the tail.

In the female it really should be the bird of curves with no hint of straight lines, and there should be a slight cushion and correctly delineated tail.

The Whites should excel in type because they are not concerned with exact lacing or other requirement. *Note the very short back and the roundness of the body.*

Figure 4.46 White Wyandotte Male

YOKOHAMA & PHOENIX*

These are of Japanese origin; known as *Onagadori* in large fowl, with exceptionally long tails, up to 30ft. long. In bantams the tails are still long when compared to other breeds, but are at the most a metre, and usually much less.

They are said to be pheasant-like and certainly, with their long bodies and large tails the overall impression is that of a Reeves or other of the large ornamental pheasants.

Combs are single or walnut or rose and at the time of writing the British *standards* give all the varieties under the group name of *Yokohama*. However, in the older standards the single combed birds were the Phoenix and the Yokohama had walnut combs.++

Colours are varied, but the walnut varieties are either Red Saddled or White. The single combed birds may be any colour found in Game and therefore are seen in Duckwing (Silver and Gold), Spangled, White, Black Reds and others.

Bantams are around, but quite scarce. They have been shown from early times, but never seem to become popular. This is a great pity because the Yokohama is an extremely attractive breed. Weights should be in the region of 22 to 26oz. (APA).

If classes are to be provided at shows a double-size cage should be provided; otherwise the tail may be damaged.

* Readers interested in the long-tailed Japanese breed should refer to the book *Japanese Long Tailed Fowl*, J Batty.
++ Rex Woods who was a pioneer in bringing back rare breeds insisted that the correct comb was walnut. See Rare Poultry of Ashe, 1976, p. 44.

Phoenix Type with single comb

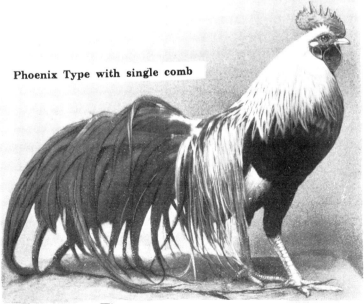

Figure 4.47 Yokohamas

RARE OR LITTLE KNOWN BREEDS

Apteryx (also known as Australian Kiki Fowl)
A cross between the Silkie and another breed; in USA with
White Plymouth Rocks and known as Missouri Fluff breed.

Coveney White (1924)
Named after a village near Ely. Cup comb like the Sicilian
Buttercup and a layer.

Exmoor (1950)
A light breed, although plumpish; blue in colour with dark
legs.

Golden Essex (1933)
Cross between Rhode Island Reds and Croad Langshan and
later Barnevelders.

Malines (1921) A Belgian breed which looks rather like a
Barred Plymouth Rock with Lightly feathered legs.

Wherwell
A heavy breed which was partridge colour in males and females were chestnut brown with black lacing.

Wyndham Black
Black with green sheen, but sex linked so pullets are recognizable when hatched (all black); cockerels white necks.

York
Similar to the Welsummer.

Auto sexing Breeds

Cambars, Legbars, Brockbars, Dorbars, Rhodebars and
Welbars are all examples of breeds which allow chicks
to be sexed on colour because the females are different
from the cockerels.

Many Others

There were many others on the British scene and, no
doubt, others in the USA where there is a tendency to
proliferate breeds and varieties. As pointed out by H
Easom Smith *(Modern Poultry Development)* there was
even a breed developed called **Droodlies!**

APPENDIX

COMMON OR GENERAL FAULTS

Many fanciers keep bantams for showing and therefore any faults must be eradicated by careful breeding. Some may be dealt with by training (eg, bad posture), but usually, if a fault is serious, the bird will stand no chance of winning. Many of these are given on page 33.

The fancier must be prepared to study the descriptions given earlier, as well as the appropriate breed standards, to learn the main contents, and to be able to recognize the faults listed. In selecting birds for show be guided by reality, not by affection for a particular bird. Many mistakes are made by taking the wrong bird to a show when it has won previously, but is now out of condition or has developed temporary faults.

This section deals with some of the common faults; others are dealt with earlier, for instance, vulture hocks and duckfootedness, are shown on page 27 and in the text for some of the breeds likely to be affected. Try to adopt a very critical approach to the whole process of establishing a list of '**strengths and weaknesses**' for each bird to be shown.

---

*Readers are referred to the following books, available from the publishers:
Art of Faking Exhibition Poultry, George Ryley Scott, which deal with showing and judging, and the new title *Poultry Shows & Exhibiting*, Dr J Batty. Also breed books on specific breeds of bantams.

Faults in Body Structure

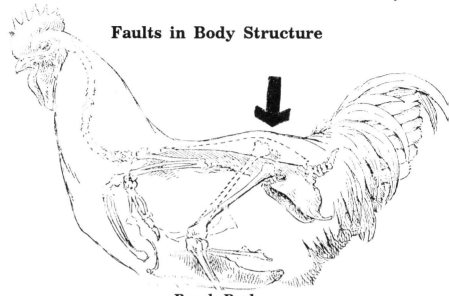

Roach Back
In bad cases the lump can be seen; in others it will be felt.

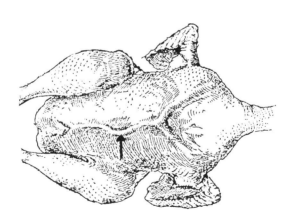

Twisted Keel
This may not be obvious until the bird is handled

Faults in Combs

Fish Tailed Comb   **Twisted Comb**

Side Sprigs   **Split Comb**
                                  Incorrect spacing

Lopped Comb   **Lumpy Comb**

Faults in Tails

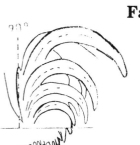

Squirrel Tail   Wry Tail

Split Tail   High Tail

Short Tail   Fan tail

Twisted Hackles
Also dry hackle a fault

Faulty Crest
Lacking fullness

Faults in Legs

Knock Kneed

Bow Legged

Faults in Wings

Split Wing

Dropped Wing

INDEX

Note: Breeds are listed in alphabetical order, starting at page 32. These are not listed separately in the index.